rockschool®

Guitar Grade 6

*Performance pieces, technical exercises and in-depth guidance
for Rockschool examinations*

Acknowledgements

Published by Rockschool Ltd. © 2012
Catalogue Number RSK051207
ISBN: 978-1-908920-06-5
Revision 1 | 8 November 2012 | Errata details can be found at *www.rockschool.co.uk*

AUDIO
Recorded at Fisher Lane Studios
Produced and engineered by Nick Davis
Assistant engineer and Pro Tools operator Mark Binge
Mixed and mastered at Langlei Studios
Mixing and additional editing by Duncan Jordan
Supporting Tests recorded by Duncan Jordan and Kit Morgan
Mastered by Duncan Jordan
Executive producers: James Uings, Jeremy Ward and Noam Lederman

MUSICIANS
James Arben, Joe Bennett, Jason Bowld, Larry Carlton, Stuart Clayton, Andy Crompton, Neel Dhorajiwala, Fergus Gerrand,
Charlie Griffiths, Felipe Karam, Kishon Khan, Noam Lederman, DJ Harry Love, Dave Marks, Kit Morgan, Jon Musgrave,
Jake Painter, Richard Pardy, Ross Stanley, Stuart Ryan, Carl Sterling, Henry Thomas, Camilo Tirado, Simon Troup,
James Uings, Steve Walker, Chris Webster, Norton York, Nir Z

PUBLISHING
Fact Files written by Joe Bennett, Charlie Griffiths, Stephen Lawson, Simon Pitt, Stuart Ryan and James Uings
Walkthroughs written by James Uings
Music engraving and book layout by Simon Troup and Jennie Troup of Digital Music Art
Proof reading and copy editing by Chris Bird, Claire Davies, Stephen Lawson, Simon Pitt and James Uings
Publishing administration by Caroline Uings
Cover design by Philip Millard

SYLLABUS
Syllabus director: Jeremy Ward
Instrumental specialists: Stuart Clayton, Noam Lederman and James Uings
Special thanks to: Brad Fuller and Georg Voros

SPONSORSHIP
Noam Lederman plays Mapex Drums, PAISTE cymbals and uses Vic Firth Sticks
Rockschool would like to thank the following companies for donating instruments used in the cover artwork

PRINTING
Printed and bound in the United Kingdom by Caligraving Ltd
CDs manufactured in the European Union by Software Logistics

DISTRIBUTION
Exclusive Distributors: Music Sales Ltd

CONTACTING ROCKSCHOOL
www.rockschool.co.uk
Telephone: +44 (0)845 460 4747
Fax: +44 (0)845 460 1960

Table of Contents

Introductions & Information

Rockschool Grade Pieces

Technical Exercises

Supporting Tests

Additional Information

Welcome to Rockschool Guitar Grade 6

Welcome to Guitar Grade 6

Welcome to the Rockschool Guitar Grade 6 pack. This book and CD contain everything you need to play guitar at this grade. In the book you will find the exam scores in both standard guitar notation and TAB. The CD has full stereo mixes of each tune, backing tracks to play along to for practice, and spoken two bar count-ins to both the full mixes and backing track versions of the songs.

Guitar Exams

At each grade, you have the option of taking one of two different types of examination:

- **Grade Exam:** a Grade Exam is a mixture of music performances, technical work and tests. You prepare three pieces (two of which may be Free Choice Pieces) and the contents of the Technical Exercise section. This accounts for 75% of the exam marks. The other 25% consists of: a Quick Study Piece (10%), a pair of instrument specific Ear Tests (10%), and finally you will be asked five General Musicianship Questions (5%). The pass mark is 60%.

- **Performance Certificate:** in a Performance Certificate you play five pieces. Up to three of these can be Free Choice Pieces. Each song is marked out of 20 and the pass mark is 60%.

Book Contents

The book is divided into a number of sections. These are:

- **Exam Pieces:** in this book you will find six specially commissioned pieces of Grade 6 standard. Each of these is preceded by a *Fact File*. Each Fact File contains a summary of the song, its style, tempo, key and technical features, along with a list of the musicians who played on it. There is additional information on the techniques and style as well as recommended further listening. The song is printed on up to four pages. Immediately after each song is a *Walkthrough*. This covers the song from a performance perspective, focusing on the technical issues you will encounter along the way. Each Walkthrough features two musical 'highlights' showing particular parts of the song. Each song comes with a full mix version and a backing track. Both versions have spoken count-ins at the beginning. Please note that any solos played on the full mix versions are indicative only.

- **Technical Exercises:** you should prepare the exercises set in this grade in the keys indicated. You should also choose *one* Stylistic Study from the three printed to practise and play to the backing track in the exam. The style you choose will determine the style of the Quick Study Piece.

- **Supporting Tests and General Musicianship Questions:** in Guitar Grade 6 there are three supporting tests – a Quick Study Piece, a pair of Ear Tests and a set of General Musicianship Questions (GMQs) asked at the end of each exam. Examples of the types of tests likely to appear in the exam are printed in this book. Additional test examples of both types of test and the GMQs can be found in the Rockschool *Guitar Companion Guide*.

- **Grade 7 Preview:** we have included in this book one of the songs found in the Grade 7 Guitar book as a taster. The piece is printed with its Fact File and Walkthrough and the full mix can be found on the CD.

- **General Information:** finally, you will find information on exam procedures, including online examination entry, marking schemes, and what to do when arriving, and waiting, for your exam.

We hope you enjoy using this book. You will find a *Syllabus Guide* for Guitar and other exam information on our website: *www.rockschool.co.uk*. Rockschool Graded Music Exams are accredited in England, Wales and Northern Ireland by Ofqual, the DfE and CCEA and by SQA Accreditation in Scotland.

SONG TITLE: MOHAIR MOUNTAIN
GENRE: CLASSIC ROCK
TEMPO: 92/126 BPM
KEY: A MINOR

TECH FEATURES: TIME SIGNATURE CHANGES
TEMPO CHANGE
SOLOING WITH DYNAMICS

COMPOSERS: JOE BENNETT
& KUNG FU DRUMMER

PERSONNEL: STUART RYAN (GTR)
HENRY THOMAS (BASS)
NOAM LEDERMAN (DRUMS)

OVERVIEW

'Mohair Mountain' is a classic rock piece similar in style to the pioneering sounds of classic rock bands such as Cream, Led Zeppelin and Aerosmith. Among its techniques it features time signature changes, legato runs and soloing with dynamics.

STYLE FOCUS

Classic rock guitar is influenced by electric blues. For example, the most common scales in classic rock lead playing and riff writing are the minor pentatonic and its close relative the blues scale. String bends, vibrato and other nuances come directly from the blues. Faster passages are not usually played using strict alternate picking. Instead they feature hammer-ons and pull-offs that are, generally speaking, less demanding in terms of technique.

THE BIGGER PICTURE

There's a distinct thread connecting the electric blues of the 1950s and 1960s to classic rock. Blues guitarists developed a style of playing that utilised the relatively low tension and height of electric guitar strings compared to the set-up of the traditional acoustic or semi-acoustic instruments. Electric guitars are made for string bends, which make for a vocal-like sound custom-built for the expressiveness of the blues. English groups like The Rolling Stones, The Yardbirds and Cream all reinterpreted the parts they heard on blues records, thus creating blues rock.

Eric Clapton was the pivotal figure in the blues rock scene. On John Mayall's 1966 album *Blues Breakers With Eric Clapton* he demonstrated a great understanding of electric blues and a virtuoso technique. His impressive tone was achieved by turning up his Marshall amp until it distorted under the yoke of a humbucker equipped Gibson Les Paul. Led Zeppelin's Jimmy Page used the same set-up to fuel many riffs like 'Black Dog' and 'Heartbreaker'.

Today, Black Country Communion, Black Stone Cherry and Kasabian continue to fill stadiums with guitar riffs inspired by classic rock.

RECOMMENDED LISTENING

Led Zeppelin's 'Black Dog' and 'The Ocean' both use time signature tricks with riffs. The Doors' 'Roadhouse Blues' is a strong and simple example of a blues boogie riff in a rock song, and Kasabian's 'Shoot The Runner' is a more recent version of a similar idea.

Mohair Mountain

Joe Bennett & Kung Fu Drummer

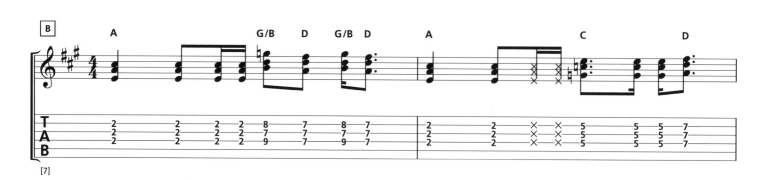

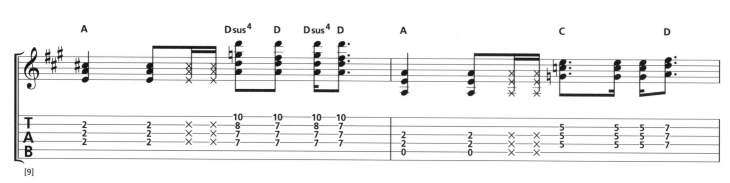

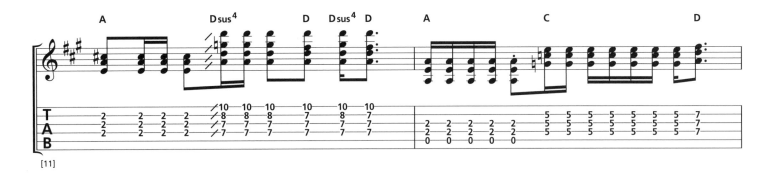

[11]

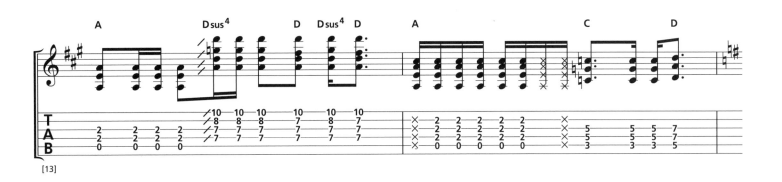

[13]

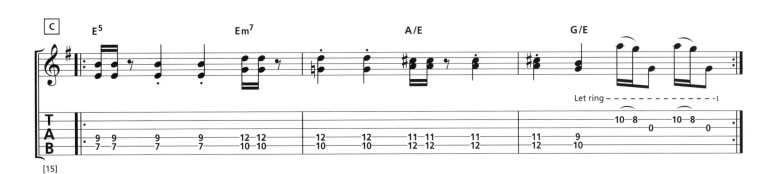

[15]

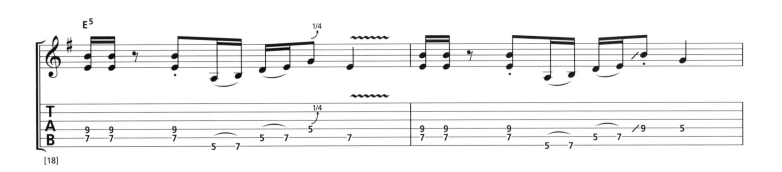

[18]

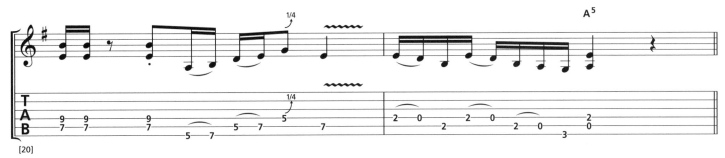

[20]

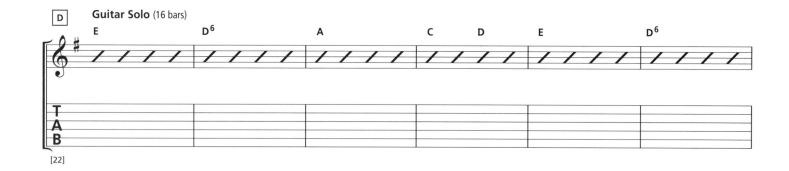

[22]

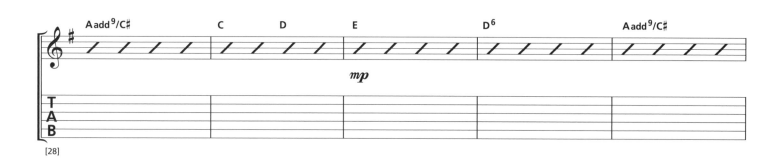

[28]

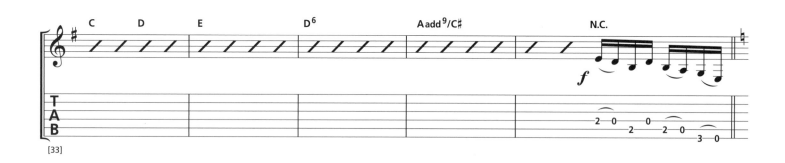

[33]

[38]

[42]

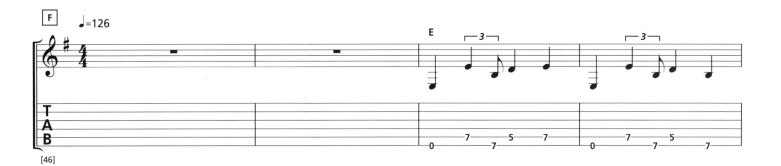

Walkthrough

Amp Settings
The overdriven guitar sound is not as heavily saturated as it first appears, so avoid the temptation to add too much distortion/gain. Boost the middle and treble to give your tone an aggressive edge that will cut through the mix.

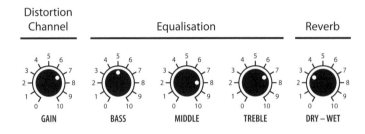

A Section (Bars 1–6)
The A Section is a single-note riff using extensive hammer-ons and pull-offs. The most challenging aspect of this riff is the movement between 4/4 and 7/8 time signatures.

Bars 1–6 | *4/4 to 7/8 time signature change*
It's common to count 4/4 as "1 & 2 & 3 & 4 &" and 7/8 as "one-two-three-four-five-six-sev". However, since the pulse of the track doesn't shift to eighth notes from this bar, another way to think of the 7/8 is to treat it as a bar of 4/4 with half a beat missing. Omit the '&' count from beat four to help you feel the groove more (Fig. 1).

B Section (Bars 7–14)
This chordal riff moves a single chord shape around the fretboard using embellishments to create extra movement.

Bars 7–14 | *Ghost strums*
A constant 16th-note strumming motion help create fluency. When you don't want to strike the strings, move your pick away a small amount so your hand passes over the strings without striking them –these are ghost strums.

C Section (Bars 15–21)
Here you combine single-note pentatonic ideas with two-note chords.

Bars 15–18 | *Three on four rhythm*
These bars feature a rhythmic idea where a three-beat pattern is placed across the 4/4 time signature to create interesting accents (Fig. 2). It may help to count through the bars so that you don't lose where the strong beats are.

D Section (Bars 22–37)
The D section is a guitar solo and features a change of dynamics halfway through.

Bars 22–37 | *Guitar solo*
Stylistically, the blues or minor pentatonic scales are the most obvious choices. However, this solo is about more than scale choices. Eight bars in the dynamic changes from *f* to *mp* and it is important that your solo reflects this.

E Section (Bars 38–45)
This is a John Bonham (Led Zeppelin) style drum solo where the guitar plays a sparser variation of the A section.

Bars 38–45 | *Tight rhythm parts*
The combination of changing time signatures and the large number of rests means it is essential that you count through the bars here. If you tap your foot, be aware that the 7/8 bar will interrupt the flow of these movements, so be careful.

F Section (Bars 46–64)
This single-note riff has a triplet feel and a change of tempo.

Bars 46–64 | *Tempo change*
The first two bars of the tempo change are first played by the bass and then the drums. Use these two bars to get settled into the new tempo/groove.

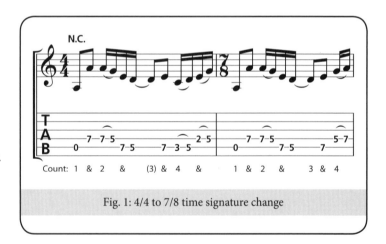

Fig. 1: 4/4 to 7/8 time signature change

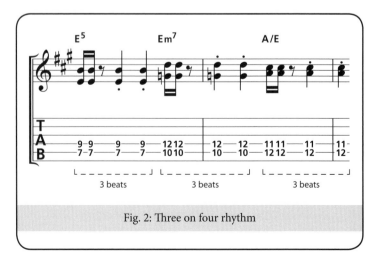

Fig. 2: Three on four rhythm

SONG TITLE: STRIPED SHIRT
GENRE: JAZZ
TEMPO: 96 BPM
KEY: B MINOR

TECH FEATURES: SLASH CHORDS
CHORD MELODY PLAYING
OCTAVE MELODY PLAYING

COMPOSER: KIT MORGAN

PERSONNEL: LARRY CARLTON (GTR)
HENRY THOMAS (BASS)
NOAM LEDERMAN (DRUMS)
ROSS STANLEY (KEYS)
FERGUS GERRAND (PERC)

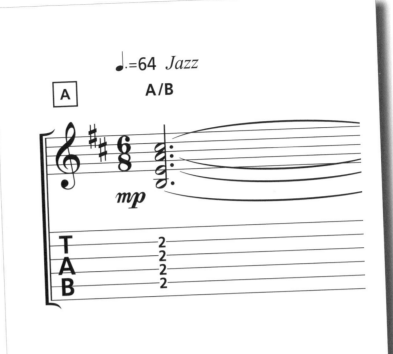

OVERVIEW

'Striped Shirt' is a jazz composition inspired by the American guitarist Pat Metheny, and played by the great session player and solo fusion artist Larry Carlton. As with Metheny's writing, this piece is full of harmonic sophistication. Although rooted in the key of B minor, there are slash chord voicings where the bass note is not the root of the chord, as well as some non-diatonic chords (i.e. chords that do not belong to the key).

STYLE FOCUS

Metheny has developed his own sound within the jazz genre, fusing traditional elements of bebop with world music including Brazilian bossa nova. Labelling him a 'smooth jazz' player does him little credit. His vast output has explored many different styles from bebop to atonal jazz and film score work. Sophisticated chord voicings and less than obvious harmony are also hallmarks of his tasteful style.

THE BIGGER PICTURE

Metheny is regarded by many as one of the world's greatest jazz guitarists. He fuses incredible technique with a sophisticated harmonic knowledge and superb compositional abilities. He was born in Kansas in 1954, and was playing and teaching guitar professionally by the time he was 18.

His early work in a trio with virtuoso bassist Jaco Pastorius brought him to the attention of the world's jazz audience, and he has achieved phenomenal success as leader of the Pat Metheny Group touring the world and performing in arenas and stadiums, a feat unheard of for a jazz artist. Metheny can be heard playing anything from archtop jazz guitar, synth, acoustic steel string and nylon string, to his unique Linda Manzer designed 42-string Pikasso guitar.

RECOMMENDED LISTENING

Metheny's early trio recordings, especially his debut *Bright Size Life* (1976), hinted at the development of a major voice in jazz guitar. He found his feet as leader of the Pat Metheny Group and his writing with keys player Lyle Mays is expressive and lyrical. The trio's live album *The Road To You* (1993) boasts his stellar guitar work. He is also a wonderfully intimate performer and his acoustic duets album with Charlie Haden, *Beyond The Missouri Sky (Short Stories)* (1997), is a personal recording of two masters and friends performing with lyricism and restraint.

Striped Shirt

Kit Morgan

Walkthrough

Amp Settings
Go for a full, well-rounded tone for this song. You may find that the neck pickup will be the best choice for 'Striped Shirt' because it has the thickest tone. A generous amount reverb will enhance the melodic parts.

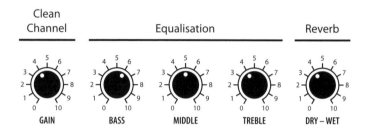

A Section (Bars 1–13)
The A section starts with sustained chords then moves to a melody that is created by picking notes from chord shapes.

Bars 1–44 | *6/8 time signature*
6/8 differs from 4/4 in that, instead of having a pulse of four beats per bar that is usually divided into multiples of two, it has a pulse of two beats divided into multiples of three.

Bars 1–44 | *Complex rhythms*
There are many rhythms in this piece that are complex, but some are easier to master by ear than the notation suggests. Listen to the CD and you should find that most of the phrases come naturally. If you find a phrase challenging, work out where against the count the notes fall and play through the phrase slowly, counting as you go (Fig. 1).

Bars 5–9 | *Picking options*
There are two picking options here. Some players may wish to play them fingerstyle. However, you will need to switch quickly back to plectrum playing at the end of the phrase. Alternatively, use hybrid picking to play the phrases.

Bar 5 | *Hybrid picking*
Hold the pick as normal between your thumb and index finger, keeping your hand relaxed. Pick the A string and pluck the B string with your ring finger. It should strike the string at a slightly diagonal angle, moving up towards the heel of your thumb. You can play the remainder of the phrase using the pick or with hybrid picking (Fig. 2).

B Section (Bars 14–31)
The B section is a flowing octave melody where each phrase is preceded by an ascending single-note phrase. The section ends with a challenging descending run.

Bars 27–31 | *Descending run*
It's best to deal with this phrase a beat at a time. Start slowly, gradually connecting the individual beats together before the connecting bars. Using a clean tone will make any slips in accuracy immediately audible, so don't increase the speed until you can play the beat or bar without errors.

C Section (Bars 32–40)
The C section is the guitar solo, where you will find some interesting chords to play over.

Bars 32–40 | *Guitar solo*
The guitar solo, like the piece itself, is in the key of B minor and although there are some unusual chords (such as $G\,maj^9$ and $F\#^{7\#5}$), the entire solo can be improvised over using just two scales. As well as the obvious minor pentatonic and blues scale choices, the natural minor scale will work over everything except the F♯ chords. Despite their complex names, the only note from both chords not found in the natural minor scale is the A♯, so use the harmonic minor over these chords.

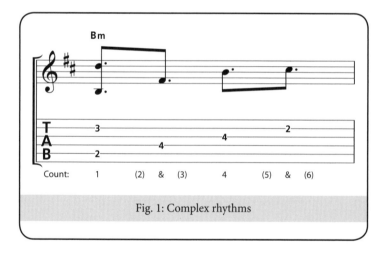

Fig. 1: Complex rhythms

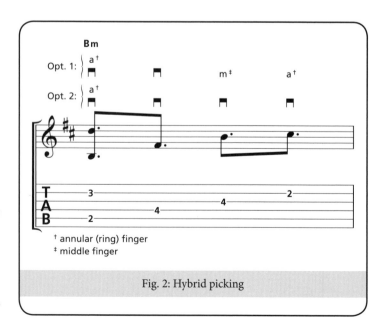

† annular (ring) finger
‡ middle finger

Fig. 2: Hybrid picking

SONG TITLE: THAT SOUNDS LIKE NOISE
GENRE: FUNK ROCK
TEMPO: 86 BPM
KEY: F# DORIAN (MODAL)

TECH FEATURES: PINCHED HARMONICS
SWUNG 16TH NOTES
TWO-HAND TAPPING

COMPOSER: JAMES UINGS

PERSONNEL: JAMES UINGS (GTR)
DAVE MARKS (BASS)
NOAM LEDERMAN (DRUMS)

OVERVIEW

'That Sounds Like Noise' is a funk rock piece in the style of Steve Vai, Rage Against The Machine (RATM) and Extreme. It features pinched harmonics, swung 16th notes, two-hand tapping and slides.

STYLE FOCUS

Unlike traditional funk, funk rock doesn't usually include scratchy 16th-note strumming patterns. Distorted single-note riffs are more typical and, as is the case here, these are often comprised of 16th notes played with a swing feel. Certain techniques are borrowed from shred, including two-hand tapping, sweep-picking and extreme use of the whammy bar.

THE BIGGER PICTURE

During the late 1980s to early 1990s, several rock musicians combined rock riffs with funk rhythms. The resulting style was a new form of funk rock notable for a high-gain distortion that, at the time, was associated more with metal than funk.

Red Hot Chili Peppers, Fishbone and Living Colour were among the first wave of this new strain of funk rock. Although he was later to adopt a rock tone and technique, RHCP's John Frusciante flaunted a high-gain sound on the 1989 album *Mother's Milk* and gave thanks to shred guitarist Steve Vai in the liner notes.

Vai began his career in Frank Zappa's band. This virtuoso's contribution to the funk rock genre was the impressive instrumental track 'The Animal' from his 1990 album *Passion And Warfare*.

Like Vai, RATM's Tom Morello was dedicated to the art of shred. In the band he was known for his mimicry of hip hop turntable techniques, but his shred ability can be heard on the fluid legato of his solo on 'Know Your Enemy'.

Extreme were operating around the same time as RATM and in Nuno Bettencourt they had a guitarist who could shred and funk with equal aplomb.

RECOMMENDED LISTENING

RHCP's *Mother's Milk* shows Frusciante at his most technical and metal sounding. 'Lil Jack Horny' from Extreme's *Extreme II: Pornograffitti* (1990) demonstrates a swung 16th note feel, and RATM's eponymous debut (1993) is littered with Morello's inventive guitar playing.

That Sounds Like Noise

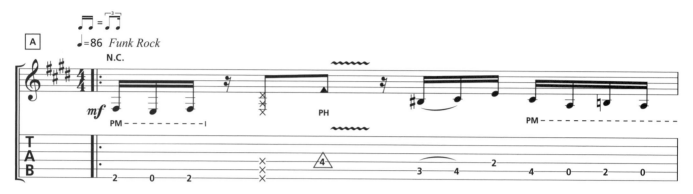

Tracks 5 & 6

James Uings

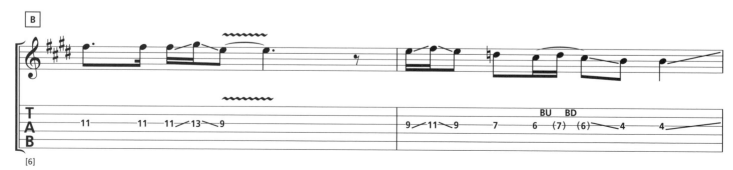

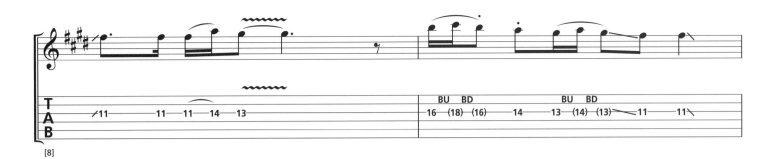

[8]

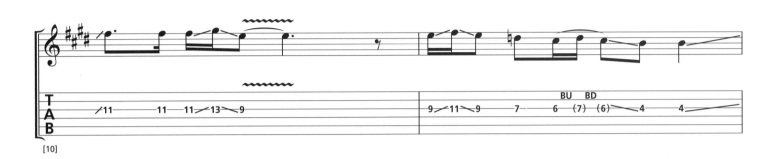

[10]

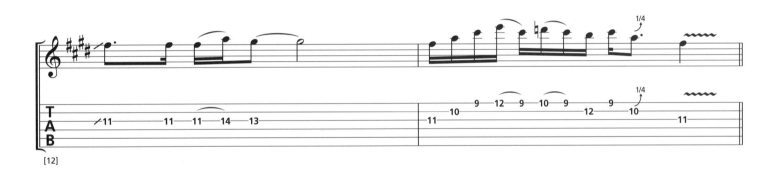

[12]

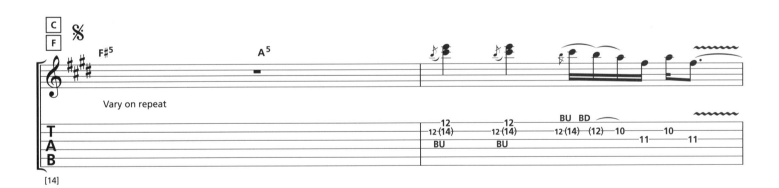

Vary on repeat

[14]

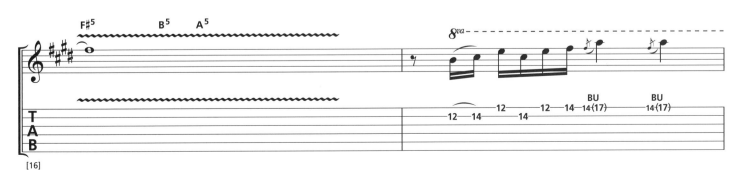

[16]

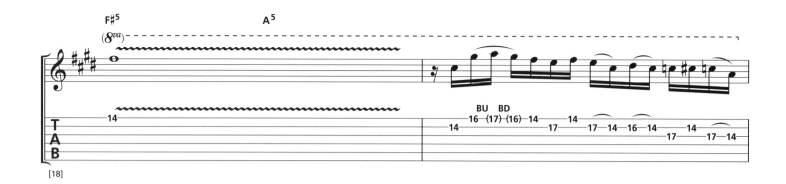

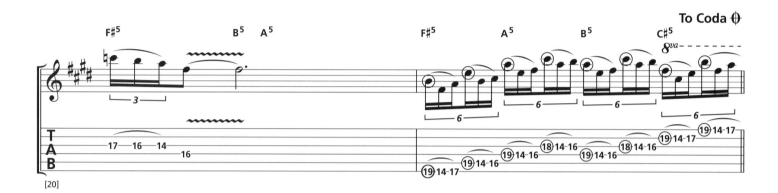

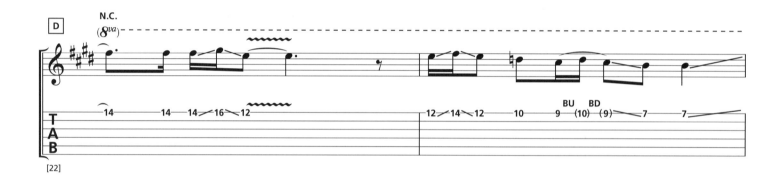

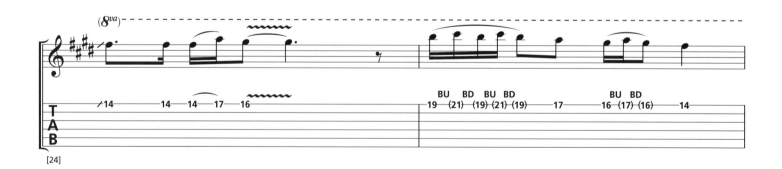

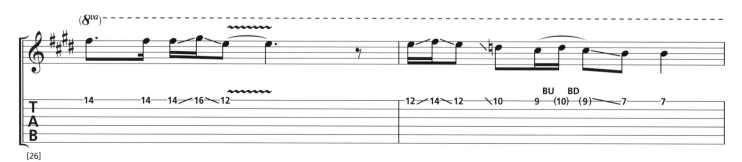

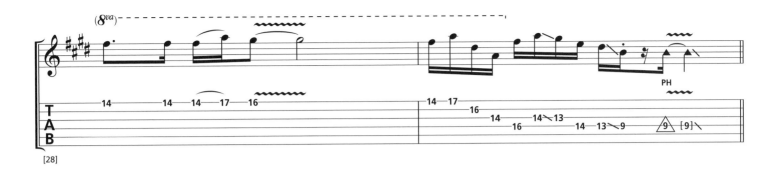

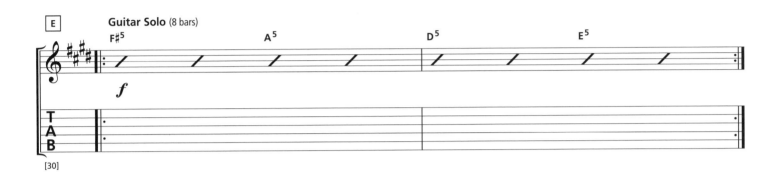

[28]

E **Guitar Solo** (8 bars)

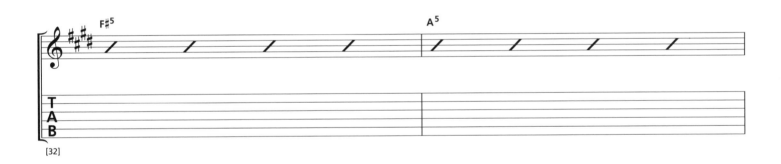

[30]

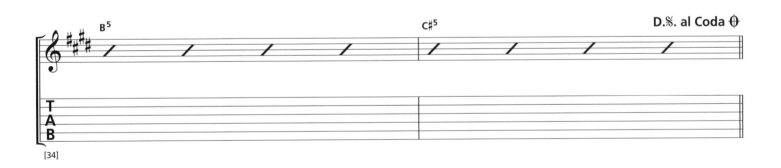

[32]

[34]

Coda

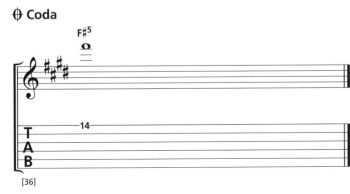

[36]

Walkthrough

Amp Settings

A smooth, high-gain distortion is a key part of this style's most famous tones. Although it's not an exam requirement, adding delay, especially in the melody and lead sections, will help you achieve a more stylistic sound. A quarter-note delay with around three repeats is ideal.

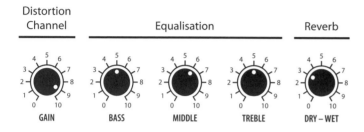

A Section (Bars 1–5)

The A section is a single-note riff built on a swung 16th feel. It uses pinched harmonics, slides and staccato notes.

Bars 1–5 | *Pinch harmonics*

Selecting the bridge pickup and using a high distortion setting will help here. Place your thumb close to the edge of the pick and dig into the strings. Both the pick and your thumb should strike the string. Pinch harmonics will only sound at certain 'node' points along the strings, so you'll need to experiment with your picking hand position.

B Section (Bars 6–13)

The B section is predominantly a single-string melody using fast slides, position shifts and bends.

Bars 6–11 | *Fast bends*

Repeatedly play the bends in this phrase slowly, paying close attention to the tuning. This will teach your fingers how far the string should be pushed up.

C Section (Bars 14–21)

The C section is a melody based on the F♯ dorian mode that 'answers' the riff played by the rest of the band.

Bar 21 | *Tapping*

The tapping pattern is based on a combination of shapes 1 and 2 of the minor pentatonic scale. Make solid contact with the tapping finger, then use a snapping motion towards the floor or ceiling to perform a clean pull-off to the next note.

Bars 21–22 | *Tapping to picking transition*

After you play the final tapped note of bar 21 and are performing the next three legato notes with your fretting hand move your picking hand back into position (i.e over the pickups) to play the next picked note (Fig. 1). Playing the tapped notes with your second finger will allow you to hold the pick normally throughout the phrase and transition smoothly back to picked notes.

D Section (Bars 22–29)

The D section is a variation of the B section. The melody is transposed by an octave and varied to include a descending run that ends with a pinched harmonic.

Bar 29 | *Crossing strings*

This challenging phrase requires a structured approach to both picking and fingering. Fig. 2 shows one possible option.

E & F Sections (Bars 14–36)

The E section is the guitar solo. Section F is a reprise of the C section with the opportunity to vary the notated part.

Bars 30–35 | *Guitar solo*

The F♯ blues, minor pentatonic scales can be used over the this solo. The F♯ dorian mode is an option and if you want a darker sound go for the F♯ natural minor scale.

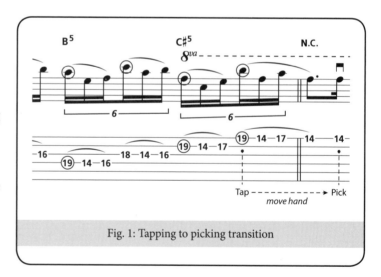

Fig. 1: Tapping to picking transition

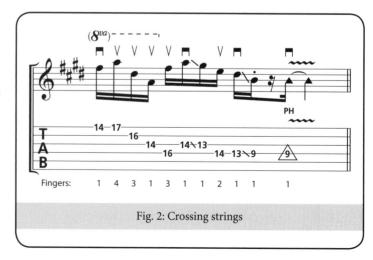

Fig. 2: Crossing strings

Blue Espresso

SONG TITLE: BLUE ESPRESSO

GENRE: BLUES

TEMPO: 116 BPM

KEY: B♭ (BLUES)

TECH FEATURES: BENDS

TRILLS

PARTIAL CHORDS

COMPOSER: DEIRDRE CARTWRIGHT

PERSONNEL: STUART RYAN (GTR)

HENRY THOMAS (BASS)

NOAM LEDERMAN (DRUMS)

ROSS STANLEY (KEYS)

OVERVIEW

'Blue Espresso' is a composition in the style of blues legend B.B. King. The piece features some typical King style playing touches from the shuffle feel to the rapid, precise bends. A major feature of his guitar style is his fast vibrato and this particular piece is all about phrasing, timing and feel. The whole tone bends in particular are a technique that must be executed cleanly and to pitch. Notice on the rhythm guitar parts how you are playing partial chords, i.e., the chord has been condensed down to three notes rather than playing all six strings.

STYLE FOCUS

King is widely acknowledged as the godfather of electric blues guitar. His extensive influence is unparalleled and he has attained a level of popularity rarely seen in the world of blues for over six decades, reaching new generations with each new album or tour. His soulful playing is the epitome of taste and he is a master of space, choosing to play just one note where most players would fill the bar. In addition, this piece is played with a shuffle feel that is a key style in blues music. Make sure your playing is relaxed and get a good sense of how a shuffle should be played. This can be a real challenge when it comes to timing.

THE BIGGER PICTURE

Riley B 'Blues Boy' King was born on September 16, 1925, in Itta Bena, Mississippi. His professional career began with humble yet electrifying performances busking on street corners. It wasn't long before word spread of his talent on guitar and vocals, and of his songwriting abilities.

One of the hardest working guitarists in blues, King has released over 50 albums and has been known to perform up to 342 gigs in a year. He commands all forms of the blues, from the soul blues ballad hit 'The Thrill Is Gone' to the shuffle of 'Everyday I Have the Blues.' His powerful voice marries his guitar perfectly and has served to widen his appeal to an audience beyond that of just guitarists.

RECOMMENDED LISTENING

King has many album credits to his name, but his 1965 release *Live At The Regal* is widely acknowledged as one of his best. In 2000, his album with Eric Clapton, *Riding With The King,* was critically acclaimed and won a Grammy award for Best Traditional Blues album. His instructional DVD, *Bluesmaster,* is also an invaluable resource for any guitarist aspiring to master this style.

Blue Espresso

Deirdre Cartwright

[4]

[7]

[10]

[13]

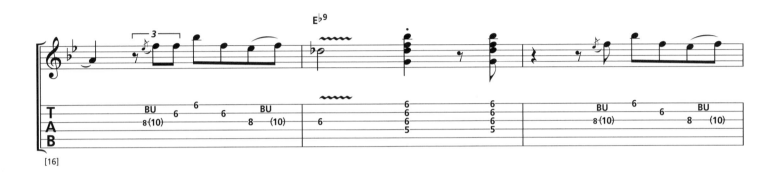

[16]

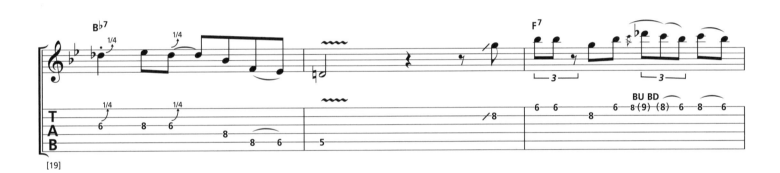

[19]

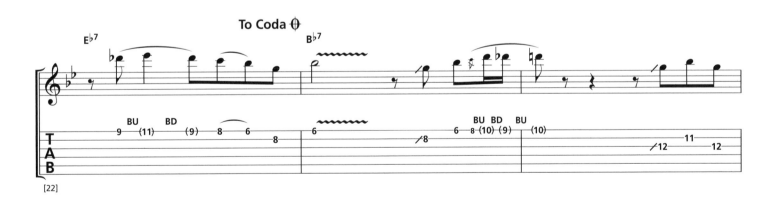

[22]

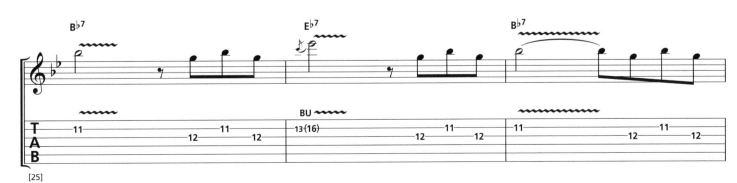

[25]

Guitar Grade 6

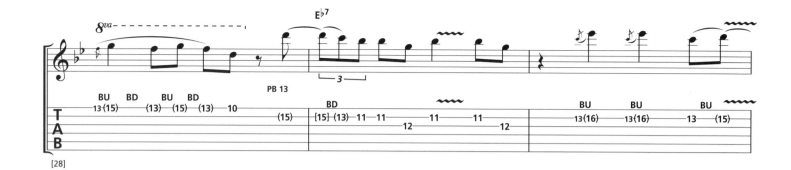

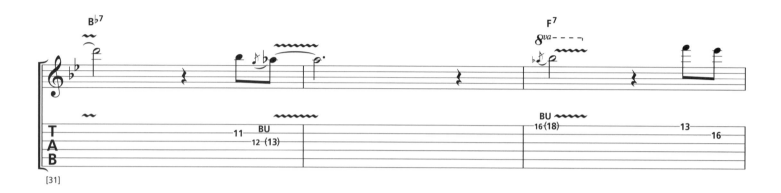

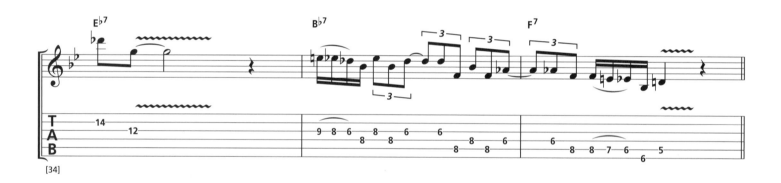

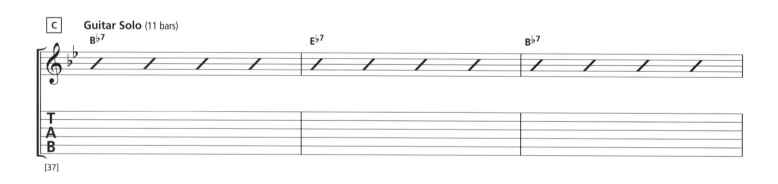

C **Guitar Solo** (11 bars)

Guitar Grade 6

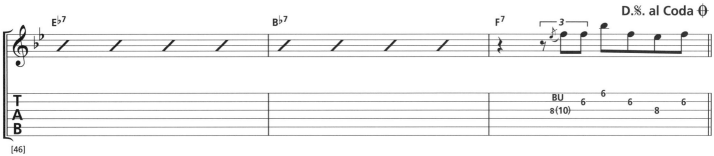

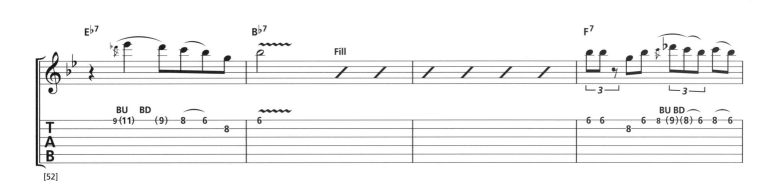

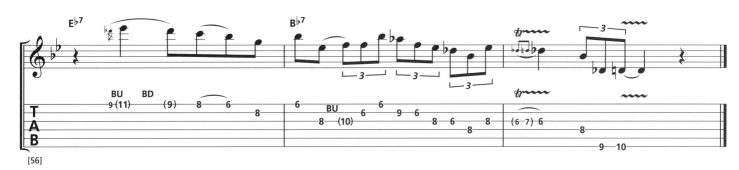

© Copyright 2012 Rock School Ltd.
This music is copyright. Photocopying is illegal.

Walkthrough

Amp Settings

Aim for a clean, well-rounded tone with a fair amount of reverb. Reverb is not like the amp's other controls – even a reverb setting of 3 or 4 is considered quite high. BB King's tone is brighter than most people realise, so if you want to emulate this you may need to boost the treble.

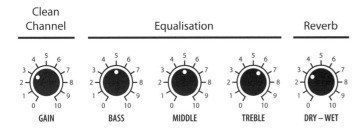

A Section (Bars 1–12)

The A section is a typical blues rhythm part that makes use of partial chords, grace notes and slides.

Bars 1–8 | *Grace notes*
Grace notes have no notational value so you should make sure the hammer-ons in this bar are sharp and snappy.

Bars 1–4 | *Fretting accuracy*
It's important that the last three notes of these bars do not ring into each other and sound like an arpeggiated chord. Play the B♭ with the tip of your third finger, 'roll' onto the flat of the same finger to play the double-stop then roll your finger back to play the B♭ again. This will separate the notes.

B Section (Bars 13–36)

The B section melody is made up of common blues techniques: string bends, trills, staccato chords and vibrato.

Bars 13–33 | *String bends*
The key to good string bends is making sure they reach the 'target note' (the note in brackets). A good exercise to help you develop your string bends is to play and hold the target note and then play the bend. Having the target note fresh in your memory will help you bend to the correct pitch (Fig. 1).

Bar 15 | *Trills*
Trills are indicated by the sign above the notation (Fig. 2). When you see this sign you should rapidly alternate between the two notes shown in brackets. In this case, the trill is articulated with hammer-ons and pull-offs.

Bar 28 | *Pre-bends*
A pre-bend is where the string is bent up to a specified pitch (the note you bend from is indicated above the notation) without being played. It is then picked and, usually, returned to its unbent position. If you have trouble playing this

phrase, try playing the lick with regular bends instead of the pre-bend and release. Fig. 2 shows a breakdown of how you can practice this.

C Section (Bars 37–48)

Here you can improvise over a 12-bar blues progression.

Bars 37–48 | *Guitar solo*
While the minor pentatonic and blues scales are obvious choices to solo with, there are several other more advanced options you may want to consider. One option is to use the relevant mixolydian mode over each chord. Some players choose to mix this mode with the blues scale. Another option is to use the appropriate dominant [7] arpeggios to outline the chord changes.

D Section (Bars 13–58)

This is a reprise of the B section where you must vary the melody before jumping to the coda to close the piece.

Bars 53–54 | *Fill*
You should create your own fill here. Aside from making sure it is appropriate stylistically, the fill should flow seamlessly from and into the notated parts.

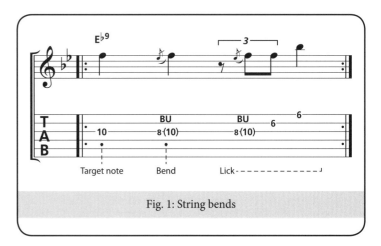

Fig. 1: String bends

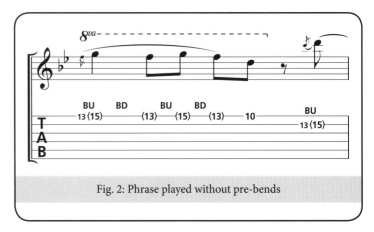

Fig. 2: Phrase played without pre-bends

Cranial Contraption

SONG TITLE: CRANIAL CONTRAPTION
GENRE: METAL
TEMPO: 105 BPM
KEY: E MINOR

TECH FEATURES: ARPEGGIATED CHORDS
SINGLE-NOTE RIFFS
NATURAL HARMONICS

COMPOSER: CHARLIE GRIFFITHS

PERSONNEL: CHARLIE GRIFFITHS (GTR)
DAVE MARKS (BASS)
JASON BOWLD (DRUMS)

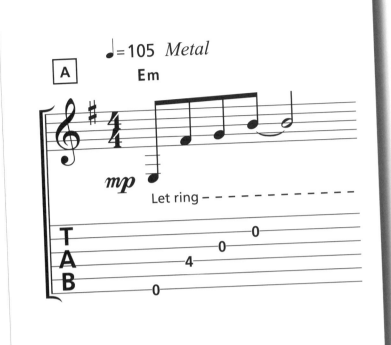

OVERVIEW

'Cranial Contraption' is a thrash/metalcore track that brings to mind Machine Head, Shadows Fall, Disturbed and Slipknot. The intro chord arrangement is played with a clean sound and the intensity builds with the octave melody, which is played with distortion. So too are the verse and breakdown sections that feature heavy riffs with contrasting low notes and high natural harmonics.

STYLE FOCUS

Metalcore is a branch of thrash metal that relies on intense playing and dark, distorted riffs that are locked in rhythmically with the bass and drums, particularly in the verse sections. By contrast, the choruses are usually more melodic. There is almost always a stomping breakdown section later in the song. The minor scales aeolian (natural minor), phrygian and harmonic minor are used with a focus on single note and powerchord riffing.

THE BIGGER PICTURE

The roots of this sub genre go back to the early 1990s when bands like Sepultura and Machine Head began to cross their Slayer and Metallica influenced sounds with the edginess and intense delivery of punk and hardcore bands like Black Flag and Misfits.

This style of metal grew throughout the 1990s and 2000s with bands including Hatebreed, Shadows Fall and Killswitch Engage who worked with strong melodic hooks. Meanwhile, The Dillinger Escape Plan infused the style with more technical playing and aggressive rap-like vocals. In 1999, Slipknot released their self-titled debut and popularised the style by maintaining a great balance between each of those elements. The genre is still growing thanks to bands Bullet For My Valentine, As I Lay Dying, The Devil Wears Prada and others.

RECOMMENDED LISTENING

Sepultura's *Chaos A.D.* (1993) was perhaps the first album to cross thrash with industrial and hardcore, while Machine Head's *Burn My Eyes* (1994) influenced many metal and hardcore bands, as did Slipknot's debut. Sweden's Soilwork are great musicians and demonstrate strong melodic hooks on *Stabbing The Drama* (2005). Mathcore is the latest sub genre to have evolved from metalcore and The Dillinger Escape Plan's *Ire Works* (2007) demonstrates how far this style has come from its ancestor.

Cranial Contraption

Charlie Griffiths

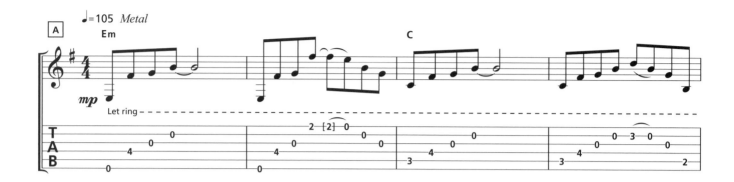

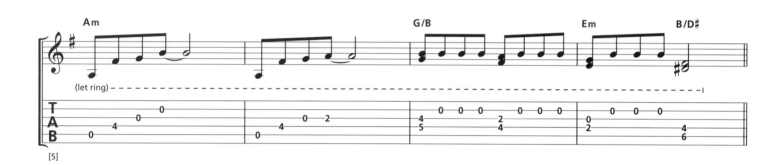

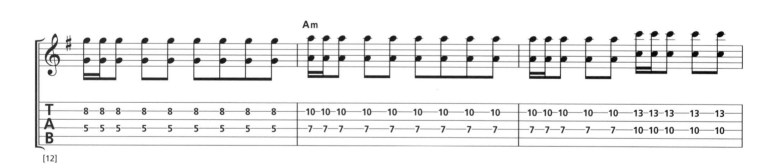

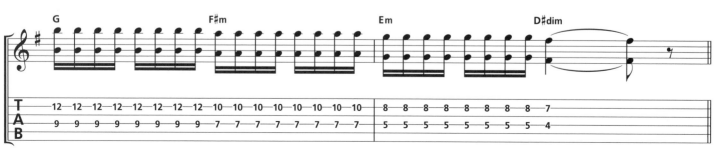

© Copyright 2012 Rock School Ltd.

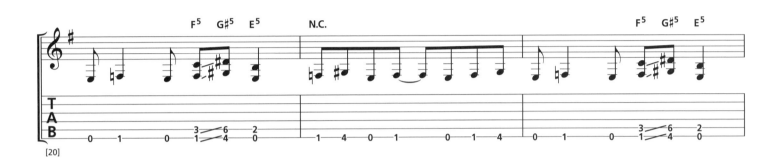

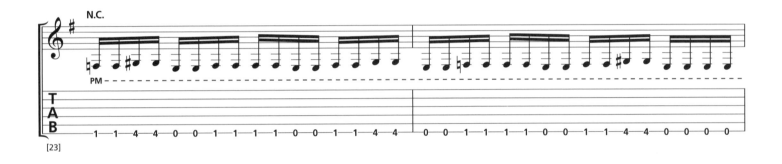

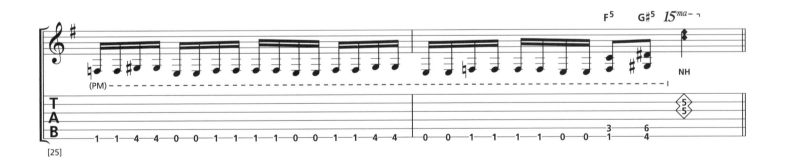

[30]

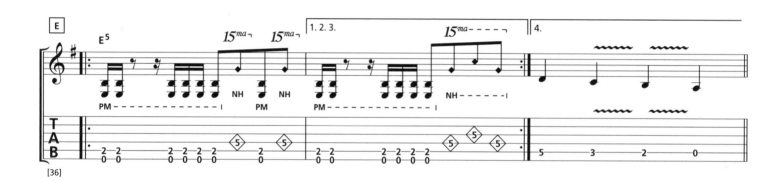

[33]

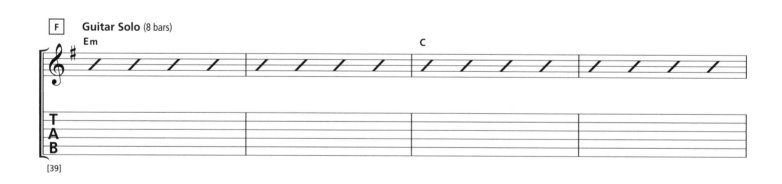

[36]

F **Guitar Solo** (8 bars)

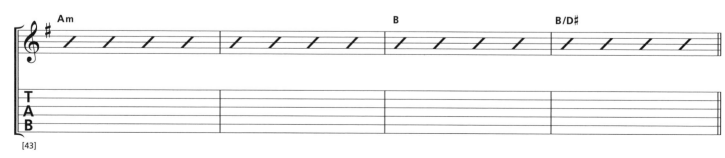

[39]

[43]

Guitar Grade 6

Walkthrough

Amp Settings

The metal guitar tone consists of two key elements: a modern high-gain distortion and a scooped tone. A scooped tone is achieved by boosting the treble and bass controls and cutting or 'scooping out' the middle. When combined with the extreme distortion this creates a heavy, aggressive tone.

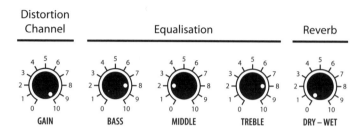

A and B Sections (Bars 1–16)

The A section is based on arpeggiated open chords. While the part uses some exotic extensions, the chord symbols reflect the song's overall harmony. The B section is based exclusively on octaves played on the D and B strings.

Bars 1–8 | *Fretting Accuracy*

Play the fretted notes with the tips of your fingers so that you can arch your fingers over the open strings. This will stop the strings from being muted and allow them to ring out once they have been played and you are moving on to the next chord.

Bar 8 | *Changing tones*

There is a two-beat gap from striking the last note of the A section and the start of the B section. Use this time to prepare to change from a clean to a distorted tone before you play the first note of the B section.

C Section (Bars 17–26)

This heavy riff is first played in eighth notes, followed by a variation played in 16th notes. Natural harmonics are used to create a dramatic contrast to the low, heavy riffs.

Bar 18 | *Natural harmonics*

These natural harmonics at the 5th fret require quick position shifts, so your finger placements need to be more accurate than those of harmonics found at other frets (Fig. 1).

Bars 23–26 | *Fast rhythm parts*

The key to playing heavy parts at this speed is to use a relaxed picking action minimising excess motion – your pick should only travel a small amount past the string.

D Section (Bars 27–35)

The D section is a melodic part that uses string bends and vibrato as well as fast, alternate picked lines.

Bars 29–34 | *Alternate picking*

These runs should be played using alternate picking (Fig. 2). They are challenging and will take some practice to master. Start slowly, working with a metronome, and concentrate on accuracy rather than speed.

E & F Sections (Bars 36–46)

The E section is a low, choppy riff using natural harmonics to create contrast. The F section is the guitar solo.

Bars 39–46 | *Scale choices*

The E harmonic minor scale can be used for the whole solo. Some people find this scale's distinctive sound too exotic to be used all the time, so you may prefer to use the minor pentatonic, blues or natural minor scales until bar 45 where the D♯ in the harmonic minor is required for the B chord.

G & H Sections (Bars 47–60)

The G section is a variation of the D section, where you must develop the original melody. The H section consists of variations of the C section.

Bars 47–52 | *Developing a part*

Develop the part played in bars 47–48. Some ways to achieve this are to vary the rhythm, note choices or articulations.

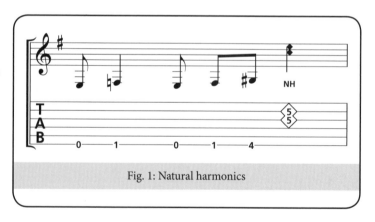

Fig. 1: Natural harmonics

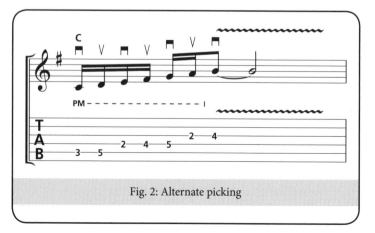

Fig. 2: Alternate picking

SONG TITLE: FAVELA
GENRE: SAMBA
TEMPO: 109 BPM
KEY: A MINOR

TECH FEATURES: SYNCOPATION

COMPOSER: NOAM LEDERMAN

PERSONNEL: NOAM LEDERMAN (DRUMS)
HENRY THOMAS (BASS)
STUART RYAN (GTR)
KISHON KHAN (KEYS)
FERGUS GERRAND (PERC)
RICHARD PARDY (SAX)
STEVE WALKER (TRUMPET)
ANDY CROMPTON (TROMBONE)

OVERVIEW

'Favela' is a Brazilian samba flavoured track boasting octave melodies, syncopation, slides and double-stops among its techniques.

STYLE FOCUS

'Favela' is a mixture of bossa nova and tropicalia. The acoustic guitar is a prominent feature of bossa nova, usually played fingerstyle. However, bossa nova can be played electric and jazz techniques such as slides and octave melodies are commonly used. Tropicalia was inspired by rock 'n' roll as much as Rio De Janeiro, so distorted riffs are not unheard of.

THE BIGGER PICTURE

Samba is the rhythmic, syncopated music of Brazil with roots in the country's African culture. The first samba record is believed to be 'Pelo Telefone', which was released in 1917 and gave the style its first significant exposure outside of the favelas (slums). It made such an impression that, in the 1930s, the nationalist dictatorship in power supported its promotion to the national music of Brazil.

Early samba records relied on drums and percussion (think of the sound of Rio De Janeiro's carnival marching bands) and was revered for its raw energy rather than musical sophistication. However, this changed in the 1950s when João Gilberto and Antonio Carlos Jobim, among others, brought in supple melodies and jazz influenced harmonies. This new style or 'bossa nova' exposed Brazilian music to the world. Its best-known song is 'The Girl From Ipanema', which was translated into English and performed by stars including Frank Sinatra.

Bossa nova's sense of sophistication and restraint made it ideal for hotel lounges and Las Vegas theatres, but new left-wing politics were afoot in Brazil in the late 1960s. The sounds and sentiment of the favelas erupted through the music of Chico Buarque, Caetano Veloso and Os Mutantes, a molten fusion of samba, rock, funk and jazz. Its name was tropicalia and it remains popular to this day.

RECOMMENDED LISTENING

Gilberto's *Chega de Saudade* (1959) is a classic bossa nova record. To hear how Brazilian music changed in the 1960s, listen to the albums *Caetano Veloso* (1969) and Buarque's *Construção* (1971).

Favela

Tracks 11 & 12

Noam Lederman

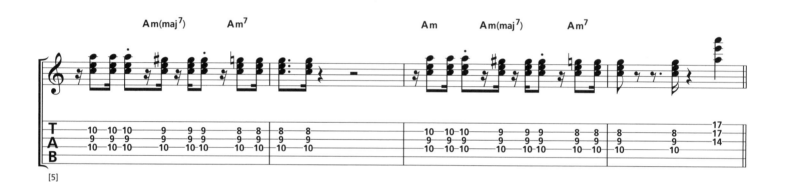

[5]

[9]

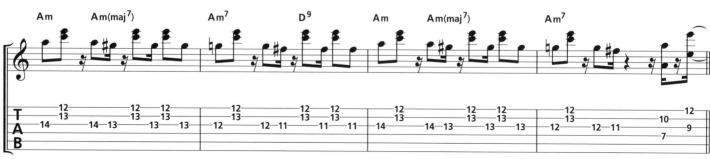

[13]

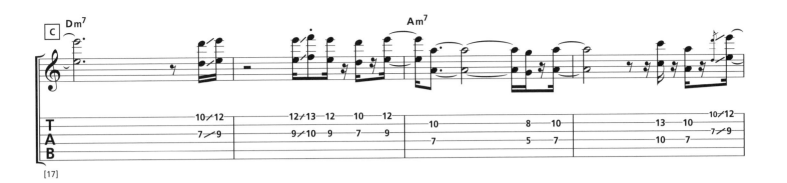

[17]

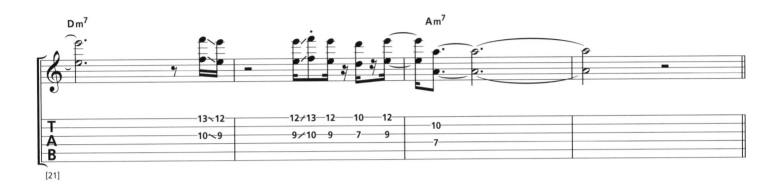

[21]

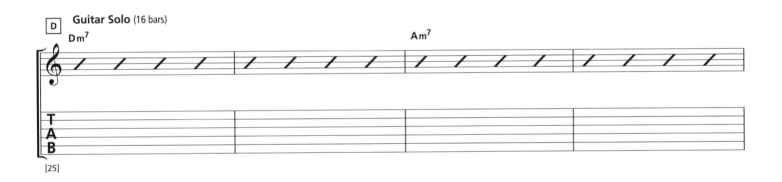

[25]

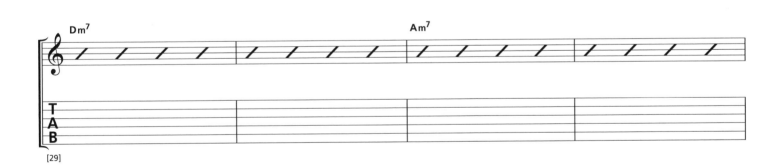

[29]

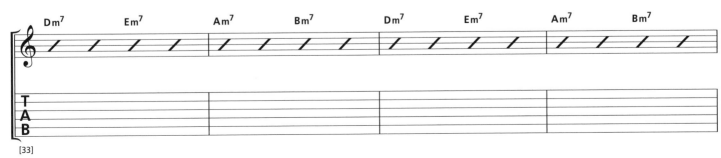

[33]

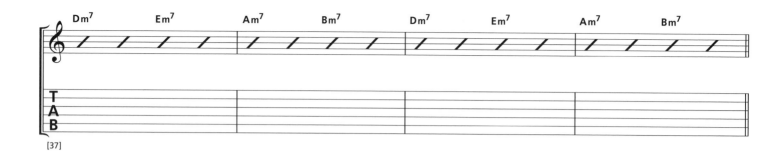

[37]

[41]

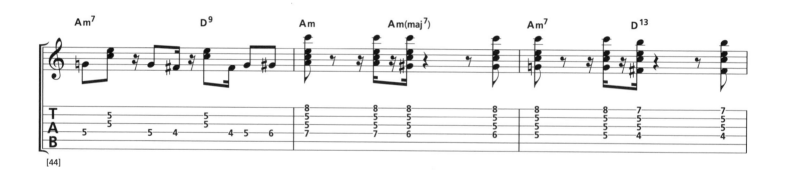

[44]

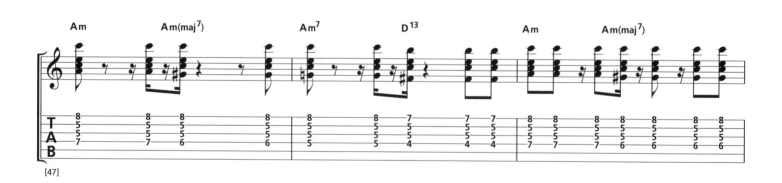

[47]

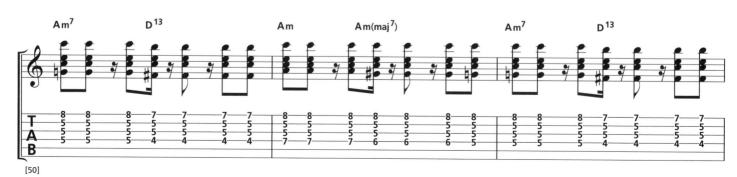

[50]

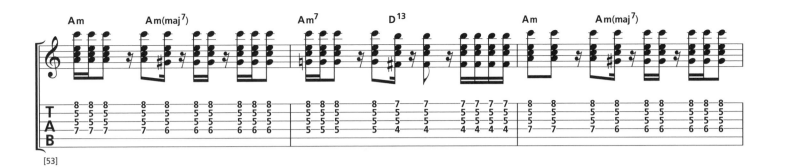

[53]

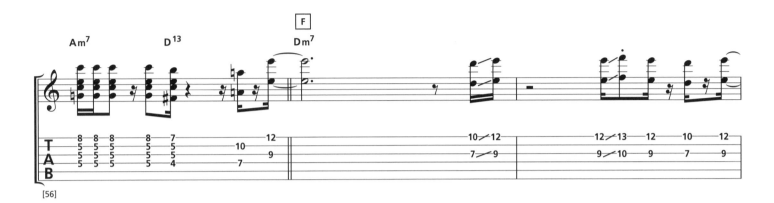

[56]

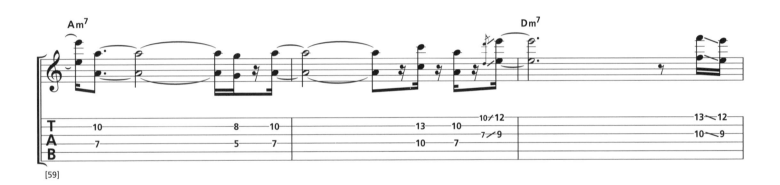

[59]

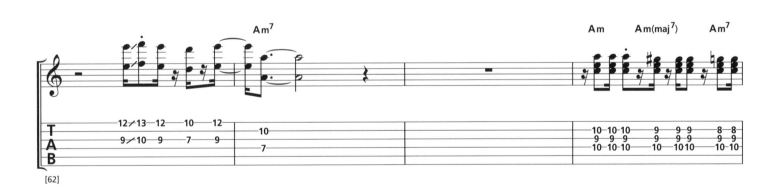

[62]

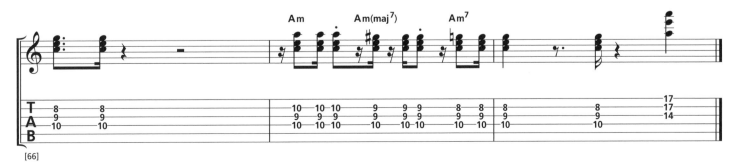

[66]

Guitar Grade 6

37

Walkthrough

Amp Settings

For this song you need a clean, full and warm tone. Using your guitar's neck pickup will help with this. Boost the bass (but don't let the sound become to muddy) and roll off the middle and treble if you feel the tone is too harsh.

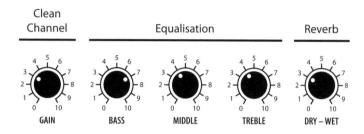

A Section (Bars 1–8)

The A section starts with a single-note melody then moves into a heavily syncopated chordal part with a chromatically descending line.

Bars 5–8 | *Syncopated rhythms*

This syncopated rhythm will take some preparation to play well. Work slowly through the rhythm while counting 16th notes ("1 e & a 2 e & a 3 e & a 4 e & a") (Fig. 1). You should work on feeling the rhythm rather than counting it to help your performance sound more convincing. A 16th-note strumming pattern will help you maintain the pulse through the numerous syncopated rhythms.

B Section (Bars 9–16)

The descending line from the A section is moved down an octave and a new rhythm is introduced.

Bars 9–16 | *Imitating a piano part*

It is possible to play this part using a pick, however the pianist plays the C and E double-stops simultaneously while a guitarist using a pick will play them so that they are slightly staggered. Fingerpicking or hybrid picking will allow you to play these two notes as the piano does to enhance the feel.

C Section (Bars 17–24)

This octave melody uses slides and quick position shifts.

Bars 17–24 | *Sliding octaves*

Approach sliding octaves in the same way as powerchords and barre chords: lock your fingers in position and move the fretting hand as a unit rather than dealing with individual finger placement. The difficulty of sliding octaves is that you must maintain pressure on the strings to keep the notes ringing. You should feel as if you are pushing into the fretboard as well as sliding up or down to a new fret.

D Section (Bars 25–40)

The D section is the guitar solo. The chord progression you will solo over is composed entirely of minor chords.

Bars 25–40 | *Guitar solo*

The four minor chords in the second half can be played in many ways. The main challenge is dealing with the F in the Dm^7 chord and the F♯ in the Bm^7 chord. You could treat the first bar as A natural minor and the second as A dorian, or bypass the F or F♯ and use the minor pentatonic or blues scales. These scales may limit your note choices, however.

E & F Sections (Bars 41–68)

The E section starts with a reprise of the B section then outlines the chord progression using syncopated strumming. The F section is a reprise of parts found earlier in the piece.

Bars 45–56 | *16th-note strumming*

Sixteenth-note strumming where the picking hand strums four times for every beat of the bar can aid fluency. The pick does not strike the string four times per beat – some of these will be ghost strums (Fig. 2).

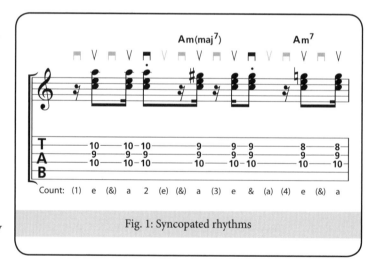

Fig. 1: Syncopated rhythms

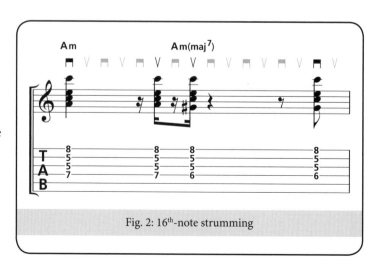

Fig. 2: 16th-note strumming

Technical Exercises

In this section the examiner will ask you to play a selection of exercises drawn from each of the five groups shown below. Groups A, B, C and D contain examples of the scales and modes, arpeggios and chords you can use when playing the pieces. In Group E you will be asked to prepare *one* stylistic study from the three printed. The choice of stylistic study will determine the style of the Quick Study Piece.

You do not need to memorise the exercises (and can use the book in the exam) but the examiner will be looking for the speed of your response. The examiner will also give credit for the level of your musicality.

Before you start the section you will be asked whether you would like to play the exercises along with the click or hear a single bar of click before you commence the test. The tempo is ♩ = 100.

Group A: Scales
The candidate must prepare all five shapes in the keys of G and B. The examiner will ask for all five shapes in either key.

1. Minor pentatonic scale (G minor pentatonic shown)

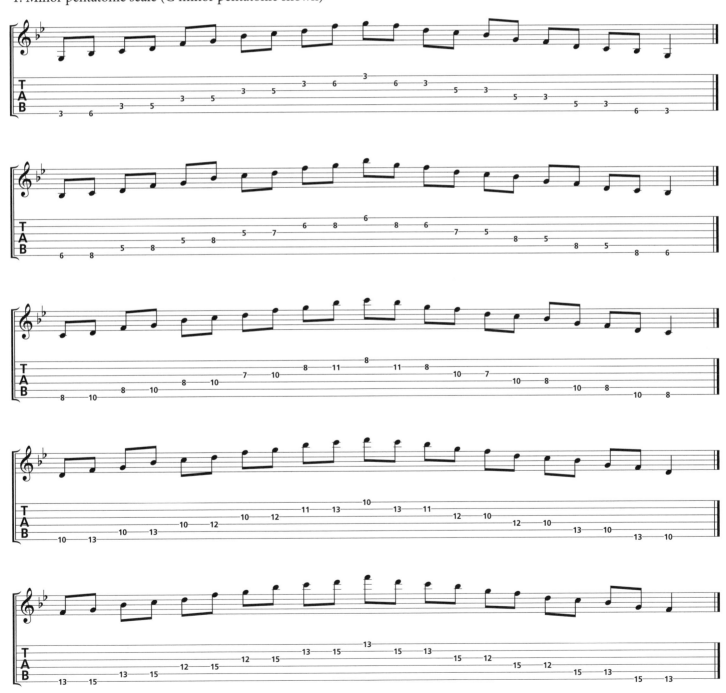

Group B: Modes

Two octaves, two positions. The first position is to be prepared on the E string from the starting notes of G–B chromatically. The second position is to be prepared on the A string from the starting notes of C–E chromatically.

1. Dorian (G dorian shown, root on E string)

2. Mixolydian (C mixolydian shown, root on A string)

Group C: Arpeggios

Two octaves, two positions. The first position is to be prepared on the E string from the starting notes of G–B chromatically. The second position is to be prepared on the A string from the starting notes of C–E chromatically.

1. Major ^{7} arpeggios (A major ^{7} shown, root on E string)

2. Minor ^{7} arpeggios (C minor ^{7} shown, root on A string)

3. Dominant ^{7} arpeggios (D ^{7} shown, root on A string)

Group D: Chords

Two positions. The first position is to be prepared on the E string from the starting notes of G–B chromatically. The second position is to be prepared on the A string from the starting notes of C–E chromatically. Chords should be strummed and then picked (arpeggiated).

1. Minor $^{7\flat}5$ (G minor $^{7\flat}5$ shown, root on E string)

2. Diminished ^{7} (C diminished ^{7} shown, root on A string)

Group E: Stylistic Studies

You will prepare a technical study from one group of styles from the list below. Your choice of style will determine the style of the Quick Study Piece.

1. Rock/Metal: tapping and legato phrasing

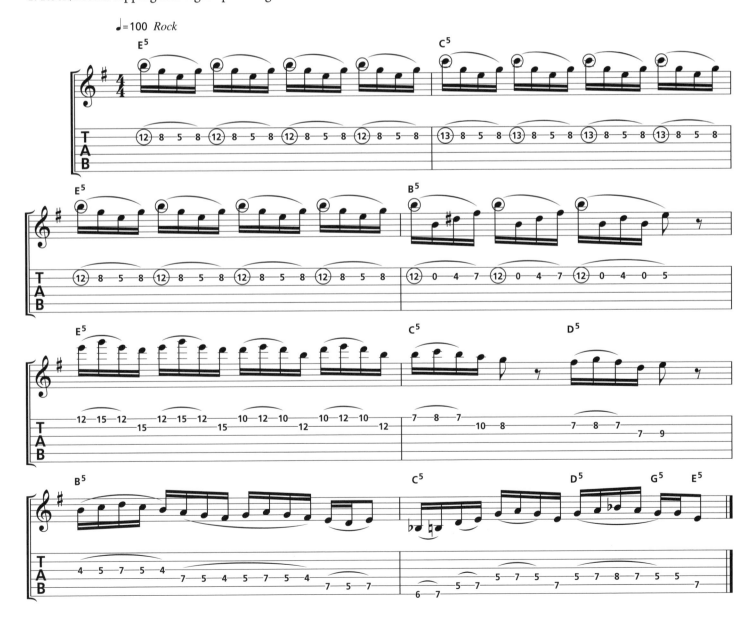

2. Funk: staccato phrasing and 16th-note strumming

3. Jazz/Latin/Blues: string bends and double-stops

Quick Study Piece

At this grade you will be asked to prepare and play a short Quick Study Piece (QSP). Printed below are three examples of the type of QSP you are likely to receive in the exam. You will be shown the test and played the track with the *notated parts played*. Any bars that require improvisation will not be demonstrated. You will then have three minutes to study the test. The backing track will be played twice more. You will be allowed to practise during the first playing of the backing track, with the notated parts now absent, before playing it to the examiner on the second playing of the backing track.

The style of your QSP is determined by the stylistic study you selected in the technical exercise section. The QSP is in the form of a lead sheet and it is up to you to create your own interpretation of the music in the parts marked for improvisation.

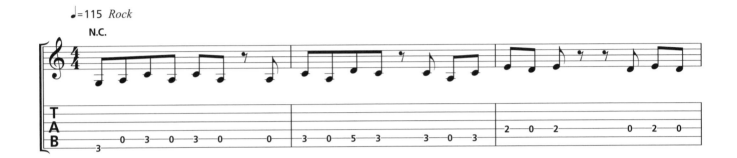

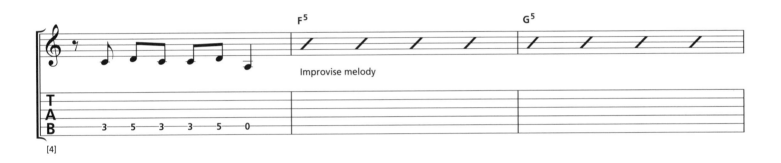

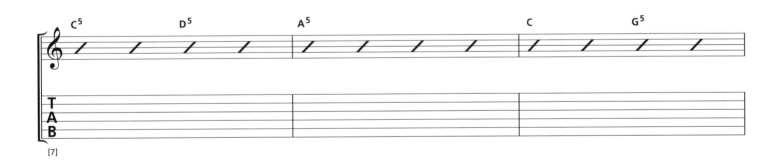

Quick Study Piece

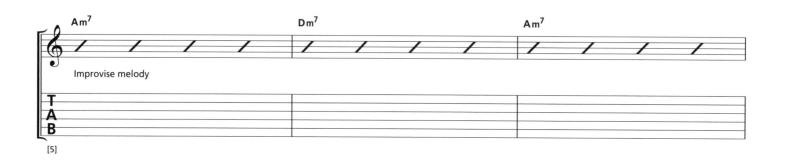

[5]

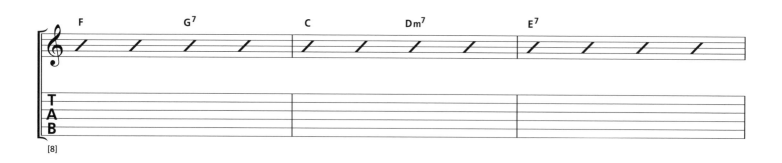

[8]

[11]

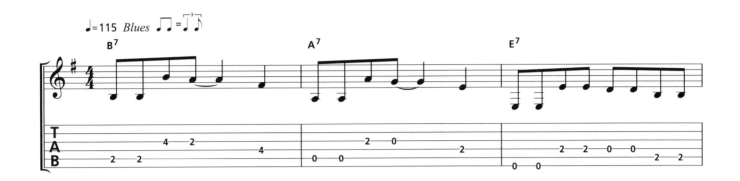

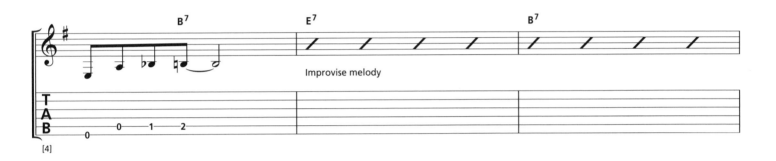

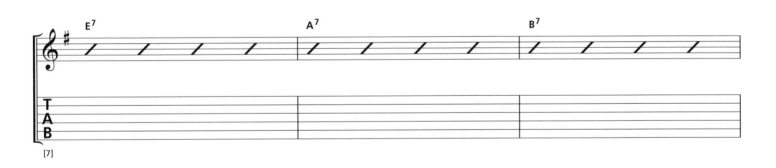

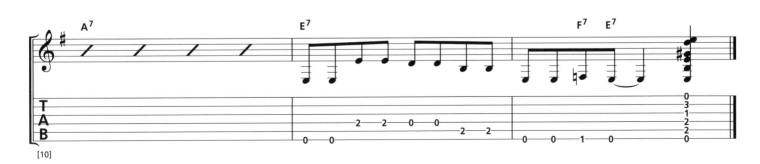

Ear Tests

There are two ear tests in this grade. The examiner will play each test to you twice. You will find one example of each type of test printed below.

Test 1: Melodic Recall

The examiner will play you a two bar melody with a bass and drum backing using either the D major pentatonic, D minor pentatonic or G natural minor scales. The first note of the melody will be *either* the root note *or* fifth and the first interval will be *either* ascending *or* descending. You will play the melody back on your instrument. You will hear the test twice.

Each time the test is played the sequence is: count-in, root note, count-in, melody. There will be a short gap for you to practise after you have heard the test for the second time. You will hear the count-in and root note for the third time followed by a *vocal* count-in and you will then play the melody to the bass and drum backing. The tempo is ♩=90.

Test 2: Harmonic Recall

The examiner will play you a tonic chord followed by a four bar chord sequence in the key of D major played to a bass and drum backing. The sequence will use the I, ii, iii, IV, V and vi chords and will incorporate a dominant^7 (V^7) chord. You will be asked to play the chord sequence to the bass and drum backing in the rhythm shown in the example below. This rhythm will be used in all examples of this test given in the exam. You will then be asked to identify the sequence you have played to the examiner, including any chord extensions. You will hear the test twice.

Each time the test is played the sequence is: count-in, tonic, count-in, chords. There will be a short gap for you to practise after you have heard the test for the second time. You will hear the count-in and tonic for the third time followed by a *vocal* count-in and you will then play the chords to the bass and drum backing. You should then name the chord sequence, including the chord type and any extensions. The tempo is ♩=90.

General Musicianship Questions

In this part of the exam you will be asked five questions. Four of these questions will be about general music knowledge and the fifth question will be asked about your instrument.

Music Knowledge

The examiner will ask you four music knowledge questions based on a piece of music that you have played in the exam. You will nominate the piece of music about which the questions will be asked. In this grade you will be asked to demonstrate your answers on your instrument as directed by the examiner. The scale question is mandatory.

In Grade 6 you will be asked:

- The names of pitches

- Any expressive musical marking found in the piece such as palm muting, accents, staccato, legato, vibrato

- Any dynamic marking found in the piece

- One type of scale that can be used appropriately in the solo section of the piece you have played and its relation to the underlying harmony of the piece

Instrument Knowledge

The examiner will also ask you one question regarding your instrument.

In Grade 6 you will be asked to explain and demonstrate:

- Where to find the same pitch on two different strings

- The function of the volume and tone controls on your guitar

- The set up for the tone required for the piece you have played on the amp

- How to achieve changes in tone in a song

Further Information

Tips on how to approach this part of this exam can be found in the *Syllabus Guide* for guitar, the Rockschool *Guitar Companion Guide* and on the Rockschool website: *www.rockschool.co.uk*. The Introduction to Tone, a comprehensive explanation of guitar tones, can be found at the back of each grade book and the tone guide to each piece is in the appropriate Walkthrough.

Entering Rockschool Exams

Entering a Rockschool exam is easy. You may enter either online at *www.rockschool.co.uk* or by downloading and filling in an exam entry form. Information on current exam fees can be obtained from Rockschool online or by calling +44 (0)845 460 4747.

- You should enter for your exam when you feel ready.

- You may enter for any one of the three examination periods shown below with their closing dates:

EXAMINATION PERIODS

PERIOD	DURATION	CLOSING DATE
Period A	1st February to 31st March	1st December
Period B	1st May to 31st July	1st April
Period C	23rd October to 15th December	1st October

These dates apply from 1st September 2012 until further notice

- The full Rockschool examination terms and conditions can be downloaded from our website. The information shown below is a summary.

- Please complete your entry with the information required. Fill in the type and level of exam and instrument, along with the examination period and year. Paper entry forms should be sent with a cheque or postal order (payable to Rockschool Ltd) to the address shown on the entry form. Entry forms sent by post will be acknowledged either by letter or email, while all entries made online will automatically be acknowledged by email.

- Applications received after the expiry of the closing date, whether made by post or online, may be accepted subject to the payment of a late fee.

- Rockschool will allocate your exam to a specific centre and you will receive notification of the exam showing a date, location and time, as well as advice on what to bring to the centre. We endeavour to give you four weeks notice ahead of your exam date.

- You should inform Rockschool of any cancellations or alterations to the schedule as soon as you can because it may not be possible to transfer entries from one centre, or one period, to another without the payment of an additional fee.

- Please bring your music book and CD to the exam. You may use photocopied music if this helps you avoid awkward page turns. The examiner will sign each book during each examination. Please note, you may be barred from taking an exam if you use someone else's music.

- You should aim to arrive for your exam 15 minutes before the time stated on the schedule. Guitarists and bass players should get ready to enter the exam room by taking their instrument from its case and tuning up. This will help with the smooth running of each exam day.

- Each Grade 6 exam is scheduled to last 30 minutes. You can use a small proportion of this time to set up and check the sound levels.

- You will receive a copy of the examiner's marksheet two to three weeks after the exam. If you have passed you will also receive a Rockschool certificate of achievement.

Guitar Grade 6 Marking Schemes

ELEMENT	PASS	MERIT	DISTINCTION
Performance Piece 1	12–14 out of 20	15–17 out of 20	18+ out of 20
Performance Piece 2	12–14 out of 20	15–17 out of 20	18+ out of 20
Performance Piece 3	12–14 out of 20	15–17 out of 20	18+ out of 20
Technical Exercises	9–10 out of 15	11–12 out of 15	13+ out of 15
Quick Study Piece	6 out of 10	7–8 out of 10	9+ out of 10
Ear Tests	6 out of 10	7–8 out of 10	9+ out of 10
General Musicianship Questions	3 out of 5	4 out of 5	5 out of 5
TOTAL MARKS	60%+	74%+	90%+

PERFORMANCE CERTIFICATES | GRADES 1–8

ELEMENT	PASS	MERIT	DISTINCTION
Performance Piece 1	12–14 out of 20	15–17 out of 20	18+ out of 20
Performance Piece 2	12–14 out of 20	15–17 out of 20	18+ out of 20
Performance Piece 3	12–14 out of 20	15–17 out of 20	18+ out of 20
Performance Piece 4	12–14 out of 20	15–17 out of 20	18+ out of 20
Performance Piece 5	12–14 out of 20	15–17 out of 20	18+ out of 20
TOTAL MARKS	60%+	75%+	90%+

Introduction to Tone

A large part of an effective guitar performance is selecting the right tone. The electric guitar's sound is subject to a wide range of variables, and this guide outlines the basic controls present on most amplifiers as well as the common variations between models. There is also a basic overview of pickups and the effect their location on the guitar has on tone. Finally, it covers the differences between the types of distortion, which is crucial to getting your basic sound right.

At Grade 6 the tone may change within the course of a piece. You should aim to use a tone that is stylistically appropriate and you may bring your own equipment to the exam room for this purpose. There is a tone guide at the start of each walkthrough to help you.

Basic amplifier controls

Most amplifiers come with a standard set of controls that are the same as, or very similar to, the diagram below. It's important to understand what each control is and the effect that it has on your guitar's tone.

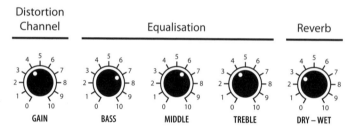

- **Channel (Clean/Distortion)**

  Most amplifiers have two channels that can be selected either by a switch on the amp or a footswitch. One channel is usually 'clean' while the other can be driven harder to create a distorted (or 'dirty') tone. If your amp doesn't have two channels, look at the 'variation of basic controls' below to see how to get clean and dirty tones from a one channel amp.

- **Gain**

  In simple terms, the gain determines how hard you drive the amp. This governs how distorted the dirty (also called 'drive', 'overdrive', or 'distortion') channel is and acts as a second volume control on the clean channel (though a high gain setting will distort even the clean channel).

- **Bass**

  This adjusts the lowest frequencies. Boost it to add warmth and reduce or 'cut' it if your sound is muddy or woolly.

- **Middle**

  This is the most important equalisation (often shortened to just 'EQ') control. Most of the guitar's tonal character is found in the mid-range so adjusting this control has a lot of impact upon your tone. Boosting it with a dirty sound will create a more classic rock tone while cutting it will produce a more metal one.

- **Treble**

  This adjusts the high frequencies. Boost it to add brightness and cut it if the sound is too harsh or brittle.

- **Reverb**

  Short for 'reverberation'. This artificially recreates the ambience of your guitar in a large room, usually a hall. This dial controls the balance between the 'dry' (the sound without the reverb) and 'wet' (the sound with the reverb) sounds.

Variations of basic controls

The diagram above shows the most common amp controls. There are many variations to this basic setup, which can often be confusing. The following section is a breakdown of some of the other amp controls you may encounter:

- **Presence control**

  Sometimes this dial replaces the 'middle' control and other times it appears in addition to it. It adjusts the higher mid-range frequencies (those found between the 'middle' and 'treble' dials).

- **No reverb control**

  Reverb can be a nice addition to your guitar tone but it's not essential. Don't be concerned if your amp doesn't have a reverb control.

- **Volume, gain, master setup**

  Single channel amplifiers often have an extra volume control (in addition to the master volume) located next to the gain control. For clean sounds, keep the gain set low and the volume similarly low and use the master control for overall volume. If the master control is on 10 and you require more level, turn the volume control up. However, you may find that this starts to distort as you reach the higher numbers.

  To get a distorted tone, turn the volume down low and the gain up until you get the amount of distortion you require. Regulate the overall level with master volume. If the master control is on 10 and you require more level simply turn the volume up. In this case, however, you may find you lose clarity before you reach maximum.

Pickups

Entire books have been devoted to the intricacies of pickups. However, three basic pieces of information will help you understand a lot about your guitar tone:

- **Singlecoils**

  These narrow pickups are fitted to many guitars. The Fender Stratocaster is the most famous guitar fitted with singlecoils. They produce a bright, cutting sound that can sound a little thin in some situations, especially heavier styles of rock music.

- **Humbuckers**

  This type of pickup was originally designed to remove or 'buck' the hum produced by singlecoil pickups, hence the name. They produce a warm, mellow sound compared to singlecoil pickups but have a tendency to sound a little muddy in some situations. They are usually identifiable because they are twice the width of a singlecoil pickup. The Gibson Les Paul is a well-known guitar fitted with humbucking pickups.

- **Pickup location**

  Basically, pickups located near the guitar's neck will have the warmest sound and those located near the bridge will have the brightest sound.

Different types of 'dirty' tones

There are lots of different words to describe the 'dirty' guitar sounds. In fact, all the sounds are 'distortions' of the clean tone, which can be confusing when you consider there's a 'type' of distortion called 'distortion'. Below is a simplified breakdown of the three main types of dirty sounds, plus some listening material to help you through this tonal minefield:

- **Overdrive**

  This is the 'mildest' form of distortion. It can be quite subtle and only evident when the guitar is played strongly. It can be also be full-on and aggressive.
  Hear it on: Cream – 'Sunshine Of Your Love', AC/DC – 'Back In Black', Oasis – 'Cigarettes and Alcohol'.

- **Distortion**

  This is usually associated with heavier styles of music. It's dense and the most extreme of the dirty tones and is usually associated with heavy styles of music.
  Hear it on: Metallica – 'Enter Sandman', Avenged Sevenfold – 'Bat Country', Bon Jovi – 'You Give Love A Bad Name'.

- **Fuzz**

  As the name implies, fuzz is a broken, 'fuzzy' sound. It was popular in the 1960s but, while still evident in certain genres, it's less common now.
  Hear it on: Jimi Hendrix Experience – 'Purple Haze', The Kinks – 'You Really Got Me'.

Guitar Notation Explained

THE MUSICAL STAVE shows pitches and rhythms and is divided by lines into bars. Pitches are named after the first seven letters of the alphabet.

TABLATURE graphically represents the guitar fingerboard. Each horizontal line represents a string, and each number represents a fret.

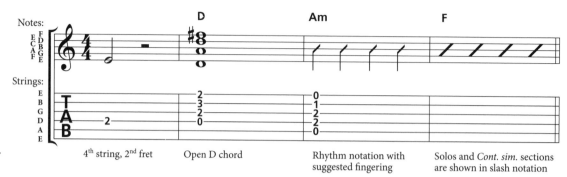

4th string, 2nd fret Open D chord Rhythm notation with suggested fingering Solos and *Cont. sim.* sections are shown in slash notation

Definitions For Special Guitar Notation

HAMMER ON: Pick the lower note, then sound the higher note by fretting it without picking.

PULL OFF: Pick the higher note then sound the lower note by lifting the finger without picking.

SLIDE: Pick the first note and slide to the next. If the line connects (as below) the second note *is not* repicked.

GLISSANDO: Slide off of a note at the end of its rhythmic value. The note that follows *is* repicked.

STRING BENDS: Pick the first note then bend (or release the bend) to the pitch indicated in brackets.

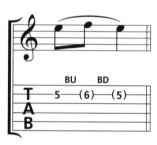

VIBRATO: Vibrate the note by bending and releasing the string smoothly and continuously.

TRILL: Rapidly alternate between the two bracketed notes by hammering on and pulling off.

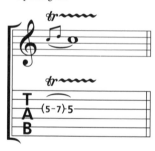

NATURAL HARMONICS: Lightly touch the string above the indicated fret then pick to sound a harmonic.

PINCHED HARMONICS: Bring the thumb of the picking hand into contact with the string immediately after the pick.

PICK HAND TAP: Strike the indicated note with a finger from the picking hand. Usually followed by a pull off.

FRET HAND TAP: As pick hand tap, but use fretting hand. Usually followed by a pull off or hammer on.

QUARTER TONE BEND: Pick the note indicated and bend the string up by a quarter tone.

PRE-BENDS: Before picking the note, bend the string from the fret indicated between the staves, to the equivalent pitch indicated in brackets in the TAB

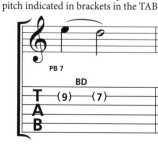

WHAMMY BAR BEND: Use the whammy bar to bend notes to the pitches indicated in brackets in the TAB

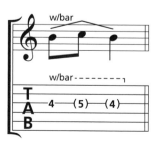

D.%. al Coda

D.C. al Fine

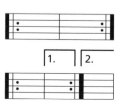

- Go back to the sign (%), then play until the bar marked **To Coda ⊕** then skip to the section marked **⊕ Coda**.

- Go back to the beginning of the song and play until the bar marked **Fine** (end).

- Repeat bars between signs.

- When a repeated section has different endings, play the first ending only the first time and the second ending only the second time.

52

SONG TITLE: THE PANTS ERA
GENRE: METAL
TEMPO: 100 BPM
KEY: E MINOR

TECH FEATURES: ALTERNATE PICKING
ODD TIME SIGNATURES
HARMONICS

COMPOSER: CHARLIE GRIFFITHS

PERSONNEL: CHARLIE GRIFFITHS (GTR)
DAVE MARKS (BASS)
JASON BOWLD (DRUMS)

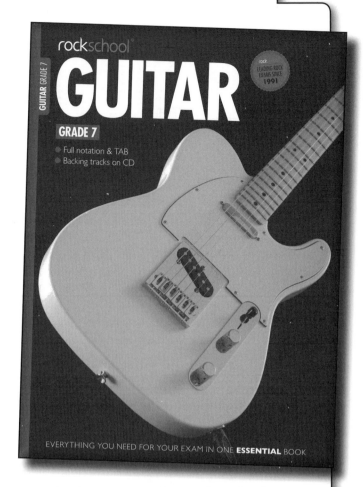

OVERVIEW

'The Pants Era' is a slab of groove metal in the style of bands like Pantera, Lamb of God, Korn and Fear Factory. It starts with a natural harmonic riff that transforms into a pounding verse riff followed by a pre-chorus in 7/8 time. The chorus is the most challenging part of the song and requires positional shifts and intense alternate picking.

STYLE FOCUS

Groove metal is a branch of the thrash metal movement that relies on powerful, heavily distorted riffs and syncopated rhythms that are often solidly locked into the drum part with particular focus on the kick drums. The blues scale and powerchords are favoured with groove metal; a strong focus is placed on technical ornamentation such as palm muting, harmonics and plenty of vibrato.

THE BIGGER PICTURE

This style of metal was brought into the mainstream in 1990 by American metal band Pantera. Their groundbreaking album *Cowboys From Hell* (1990) helped them to dominate the scene for the entire decade. Guitarist Dimebag Darrell and his drummer brother Vinnie Paul created a style of aggressive yet precise riffing with an unparalleled rhythmic power that became the blueprint for the genre that is still used to this day. Since Pantera disbanded in 2003 and Dimebag's untimely death in 2004, bands like Lamb of God and Killswitch Engage have filled the void, spearheading a resurgence of interest in the genre. More recently, bands such as Meshuggah and Periphery have taken the style to new, more rhythmically complex heights.

RECOMMENDED LISTENING

The title track from Pantera's *Cowboys From Hell* is the nucleus of groove metal. Next came the metal classic 'Walk' from their more aggressive follow-up album *Vulgar Display Of Power* (1992). Lamb of God's 'Redneck' from *Sacrament* (2006) could be viewed as a tribute to Dimebag's signature riffing style, such is the similarity. Killswitch Engage demonstrated deft guitar and drum unison work on 'My Last Serenade' from their acclaimed album *Alive Or Just Breathing* (2002). Meshuggah's 'Stengah' from *Nothing* (2002) illustrates that rhythmic complexity is no barrier to groove, while Periphery's 'Icarus Lives!' from their 2010 eponymous debut is one of the catchiest riffs to emerge in recent years.

The Pants Era (Grade 7 Preview)

Charlie Griffiths

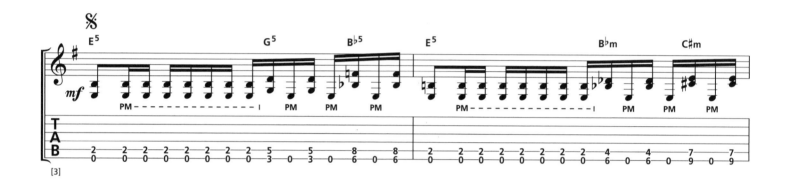

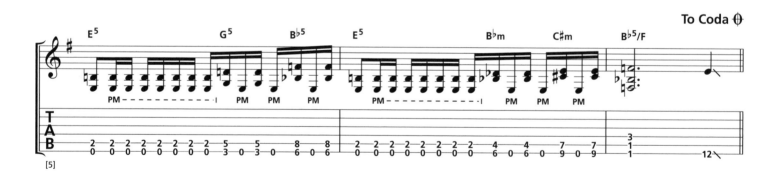

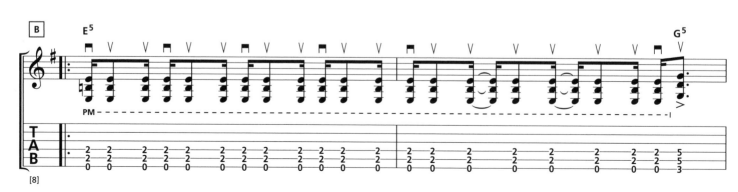

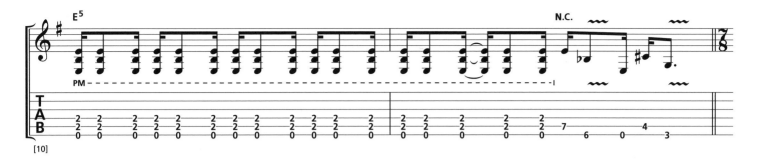

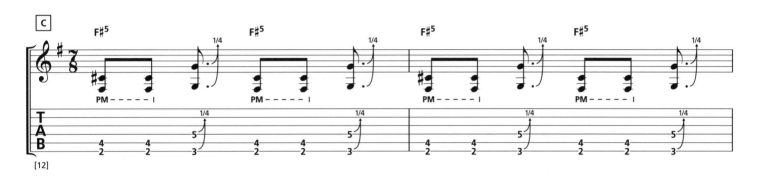

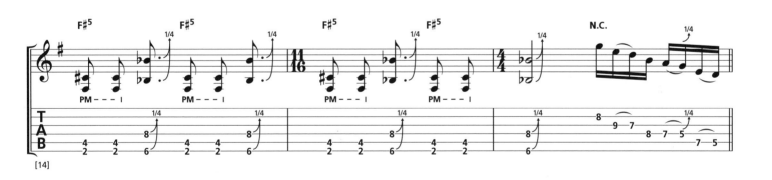

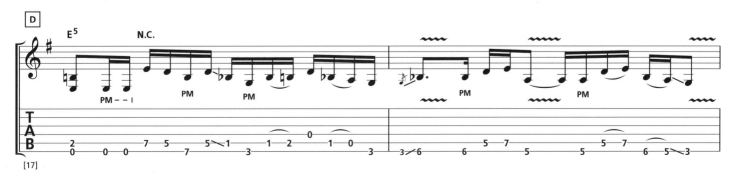

Guitar Grade 6

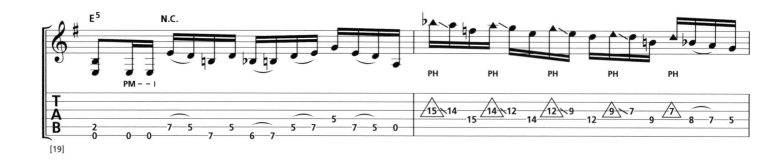

Guitar Grade 6

Guitar Solo (12 bars)

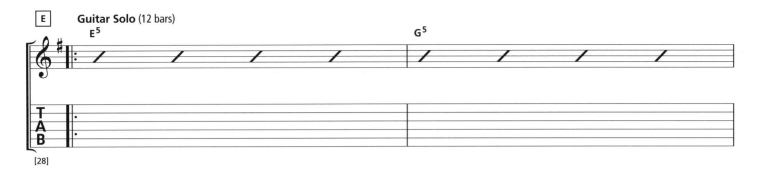

[28]

D.%. al Coda ⊕

Play 3 times

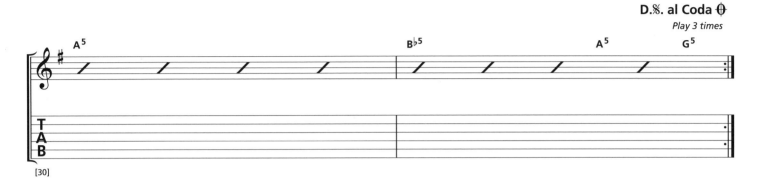

[30]

⊕ **Coda**

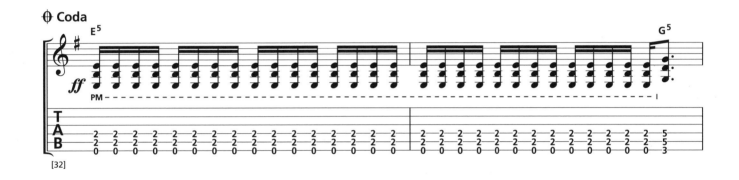

[32]

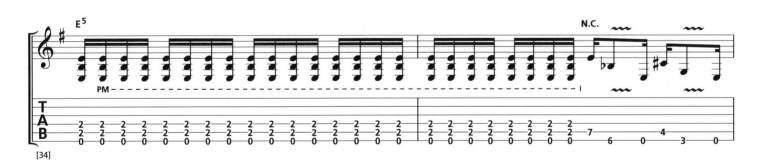

[34]

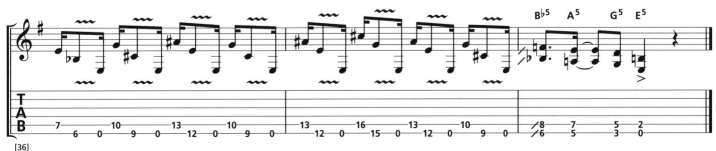

[36]

Walkthrough (Grade 7 Preview)

Amp Settings

The metal rhythm guitar tone consists of two key elements: a modern high-gain distortion and a scooped tone. A scooped tone is achieved by boosting the treble and bass controls and cutting or 'scooping out' the middle. When combined with the extreme distortion this creates a heavy, aggressive tone. Add more middle to your lead tone if you wish.

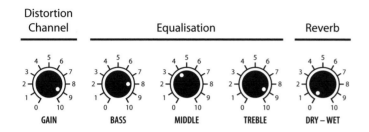

A Section (Bars 1–7)

The A section starts with a riff that combines the open E string with natural harmonics. This riff is then developed using two-note chords.

Bars 1–2 | *3rd fret harmonics*

3rd fret harmonics are a little different from those found at the 5th, 7th and 12th frets. Rather than placing your finger directly over the fret, you should place your finger *slightly* in front of the fret (towards the 4th fret).

B & C Sections (Bars 8–16)

Here is a chunky syncopated, palm-muted riff that ends with a tri-tone motif developed in the coda. The C section is a seemingly complex riff that uses odd time signatures and octave bends before finishing with a scalic run.

Bars 12–16 | *Odd time signatures*

Although these signatures look complex, the riffs have a strong groove so you may find you can learn them by ear. If you struggle with any sections, try counting the rhythms in groups of the smallest time unit that can be used to successfully divide the bar. In this case, 16th notes (Fig. 1).

Bar 15 | *11/16 time signature*

When playing the 11/16 bar, it helps to ignore the time signature and simply continue playing the riff that was established in the previous three bars. When the second A♯ is played, mentally count this as beat one (it's the first note of the bar of 4/4), listen for the hi-hat on beat two then play the descending riff starting on beat three.

Bars 12–16 | *Octave bends*

These octave bends are performed by pulling both strings down towards the floor. This not a precise movement and it is almost impossible to bend the strings by the same amount.

In fact, it is the discordance created by the 'inaccurate' bends that gives the riff its unique sound.

D Section (Bars 17–27)

The D section is a single-note riff that uses different techniques. There are many complex phrases in this section and you will have to break them down into individual beats to work on fingerings, pick directions and overall accuracy.

Bar 20 | *Pinch harmonic slides*

In this phrase you will play the pinch harmonic on the first of each sequence of three notes then slide down the fretboard to the next note. The harmonic sound will carry on to the next note.

E Section (Bars 28–38)

The E section is the guitar solo. The song finishes by reprising part of the A section before developing part of the B section.

Bars 28–31 | *Guitar solo*

The minor pentatonic and blues scales are popular in groove metal. You can also use the natural minor scale with the ♭5 added (Fig. 2). This will give you more note choices, while retaining the bluesy quality that is typical of the style.

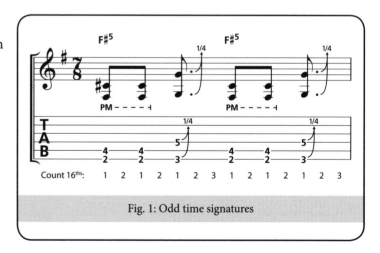

Fig. 1: Odd time signatures

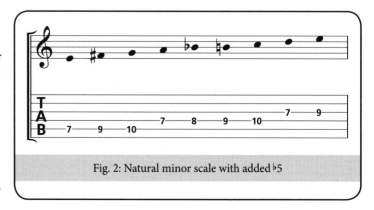

Fig. 2: Natural minor scale with added ♭5